Where are the grown-ups?

A True Story

RUTH BADLEY

First Published 2019 by Inglebooks, Mount Bures

Copyright © Ruth Badley 2019

The moral right of the author has been asserted

ISBN: 978-1-9161195-0-5

INGLEBOOKS

For Sylvia and Rose

PART ONE

1

Mother
Outer London, May 2015

You feared it would end like this. Two adult children, called to an airless room, mumbling thanks, as the hospital consultant prepares to break the bad news in the kindest way he can. My brother is attentive, accepting even, but as the expert offers his sympathies, the voice inside my head screams, 'No, you're wrong! That's not how she is at all!'

The consultant briefly meets my gaze and sees a daughter in denial. He must deal with people like me every day. Perhaps he expects a feisty response but instead I focus on the whiteness of his shirt, wondering if he has a wife or a mother waiting for him at home.

'When I pop my clogs', you used to say, and we would laugh at such a silly expression. Death reduced to a cartoon image. Now it's happening, and it hurts. Carrying on as a bedridden invalid is just not the kind of life you want to hang on to. You've had a week in this hospital to try it out and that's enough, I can tell.

A phone call in the early hours brought us, your children and grandchildren, back here to this peculiar limbo where it's possible to know and at the same time, not know. We take it in turns to hold your hands and watch you breathe, and we notice when the rhythm of that breathing changes. I summon a nurse.

She explains that the long pause between breaths is a sign your body is shutting down, but it's as if she's speaking through water and in another language. I catch the phrase, 'end of life' and just two breaths later, your hand in mine, I sense you've gone.

Was it only a week ago, that I sat on a comfortless plastic chair by your bed, listening to you talking in what you would've described as 'gobbledygook?' It didn't make sense to anyone else, but I knew what you were asking for and why you kept repeating those strange sounds.

I told them you wanted your own night clothes and when you looked at me the expression in your eyes was triumphant. I heard you make that funny little affirmative sound at the back of your throat that you always used to make when something had gone your way.

You knew who we were and sometimes your words came out right. I heard you say, 'I'm not the same'. I asked if you knew what had happened. You turned your sad blue eyes towards me and shook your head.

"You've had a stroke, Mum."

I watched as you took in that information, your eyes looking up to the ceiling and then closing. I knew what you were thinking.

When you opened your eyes, you looked back at me and a tear rolled down your cheek. A single tear from the great well of grief that weighed you down and kept us apart from each other.

A nurse arrived to distract us with practicalities. "Sylvia, I'm going to make you a bit more comfortable. I'm going to change your position, is that alright?"

You turned your head when she said your name and whispered what we took to be a compliant 'OK' as she prepared to ease you up the bed. The pressure of the pillows had flattened the hair on one side of your head and I made a feeble attempt to rectify the damage. I lacked the hairdresser's skill and I wondered why you didn't snatch the comb from my hand in impatience. You see, I was still so optimistic at that point, but you knew how it would go. You'd seen it all before from the bedside, first with Dad and then David. All the expert interventions would come to nothing and you would slowly drift away. Not yet, though. There was still the essence of you lying in that bed.

On a different day, I could tell that you recognised my necklace and perhaps it reminded you of the jewellery you wore. Some movement had returned to your right hand and I saw you twisting the hospital name tag on your left wrist round and round. I knew you were thinking, "What's this rubbishy bracelet they've given me?"

As the days went by, you grew impatient and so did we. The misplaced feeding tube, the endless explanations and delays whilst the medics pored over x-rays, trying to make sense of why the correct path to your stomach was so elusive.

On the fourth day you became agitated, suddenly pushing me away and crying out, "Go back!"

"Go back? To Dubai?"

"Yes."

There was a finality in your tone that frightened me. "I'll go back when you're a little better, Mum."

Raising your right hand, you waved such a ridiculous notion away.

As ever, you weren't too impressed with my choice of clothes. I only had time to throw a few things in a case and I wasn't thinking straight. Flying in from the relentless heat of Dubai to an unreliable UK spring presented too many variables, not least the stifling micro-climate of an NHS hospital. On these wards, sickness and dependency cocoon the vulnerable in a blanket of uninterrupted, artificial warmth, regardless of the vagaries of the season. I had too many layers on that day and you kept pulling at my blouse. The feel of the material seemed to annoy you. I had a sleeveless vest on underneath, so I removed the offending outer layer and when I did you seemed a little calmer.

As I pushed back my hair, you reached out with your left hand to feel my dangly earrings brush the skin of your fingers, and then your hand moved to touch my face. We stayed like that for what seemed like hours, looking at each other, as if for the first time. As I leaned in closer you lifted both your arms and they closed around me. Those unplanned, uninhibited gestures, free from judgement, felt like love.

It was so long ago when you first talked about the things you had and who you wanted them to go to. Now I wear the rings you wore and when I put them on, my hands turn into yours. If water has memory maybe it's also true of stones and metals. The old cut diamonds on Aunt Becky's engagement ring sparkle as they catch the light. The largest central stone has a characterful black spot of uncrystallised carbon, visible at its heart. A flawed diamond passed along the years, from Becky, to you and now to me. A bittersweet inheritance.

2

Daughter
Dubai, September 2015

Four months after she died and I'm back in Dubai, but my mind is dislocated, disordered and the tears come without warning.

At first the artificial landscape of the mall has the desired effect. I feel mildly sedated in this synthetically perfumed, temperature-controlled environment, but all the while my subconscious remains alert and free to roam where it will. Day after day it leads me back to the one place in Dubai guaranteed to intensify the loss.

She told me, with a laugh in in her voice, that she'd left the glass figurine of a naked woman to my husband in her will. Her laugh is still in my head when I find myself, as if in a trance, looking for a similar piece amongst the lavish displays in the mall's *Lalique* boutique. A solitary male assistant, eager for a sale, is immediately at my elbow, and I retreat, mute, disturbed by the attention and the impulse that propelled me in there.

A display in a fashionably affordable chain store catches my eye and, as if guided by an invisible hand, I select an item on the rail. Inexplicably, I reach for the same elegant cream tunic I purchased months before, as a gift for her birthday. It's as if I'm sleepwalking. Awareness, like an electric shock, jolts me back to

7

reality. I slam the item back on the rail and scrabble in my bag for a tissue, hoping no one notices my distress.

She was already in hospital by the time the present arrived, but even as I was folding and wrapping it, I imagined her ripping the paper in anticipation and holding the garment up against herself at the mirror to see the movement of the floaty fabric. Shorter than most, with wide hips and tiny wrists, buying off the peg relied on the skill of a trusted seamstress.

Only after trying it on, minutely examining the fit from all angles, mentally noting if improvements were required, would she open the enclosed birthday card. She might have smiled at my jokey note before arranging the card on the kitchen windowsill with the others. The new addition to the wardrobe would be assimilated in the usual way, by careful arrangement on a hanger to avoid creasing. A contender for a first outing and the compliments it would attract the following afternoon.

I would learn if my purchase had been well judged during the next Skype call. If the gift had pleased her, she would have asked if the same item was available in other colours and I would know because I'd already anticipated the question.

The pleasure I hoped the surprise would bring came to nothing. I stood at her front door, unable to speak as the smiling postman reunited me with the envelope bearing my own handwriting, posted in hope from Dubai, several weeks earlier.

Mum is not here, nor there and yet she is everywhere. After the funeral she followed me back to Dubai and visited me in different ways. Flashbacks of the last day, around her hospital bed, silently willing her to breathe, are frequent. Her shrinking frame and the dried blood on her mouth when the pneumonia set

8

in, catch me out in the middle of unrelated conversations. Vivid dreams replay the moment she caressed my face and held me in her arms, invading my sleep, waking me, usually close to tears, several times a night.

I start to see everything through her filter. She would have loved the lavish consumption of Dubai, the excess, the glamour, the wealth, the status, the upmarket shopping, luxurious hotels, and the dressing up. I had so much more to tell her about my crazy expat life out here.

When I walk through the souk I only see the beaded evening bags and costume jewellery that I could have bought her, more pretty things, to add to the existing collections we discovered in almost every room of the house. We would never have been permitted to open the door on those neatly placed possessions, much less rummage through them in her lifetime. At first, my brother and I were tentative, reluctant onlookers, paralysed by the extent of it.

In one wardrobe, what looked to be a single row of some twenty handbags on a high shelf, (neutral colours, strictly arranged from light to dark, left to right), turned out to be three rows deep when I stood on a chair for a better look.

Opening each cupboard and seeing the absolute order of it all was unbearable. The urge to disrupt was overwhelming and thinking of it brings me back to that room and the way I sought to punish those lifeless garments.

Pulling hard at a row of pristine jackets, I deliberately throw them to the floor, letting the empty hangers bang against the wood. Punching the chest of an expensive winter coat, I push until everything bunches together at one end in a metallic shriek, the

9

hangers scraping across the rail. On my knees, I toss shoes and boots out of their allotted positions, noting how her troublesome feet forced the leather into an obedient, alternative shape. It's a warm day and the effort of the task makes me sweat. I pause and feel only shame and guilt at the sight of a haphazard pile of has-beens, destined for the charity shop. I long for her to somehow stop me from vandalising her carefully crafted image but in that room of open doors there is only silence.

On another day, I came across all the old photographs. Among the many neatly stacked folders of old black and white family snaps, one of myself, aged about three, catches my eye. It was taken in the garden of my parent's first home in Castle Road, Northolt. The image ignites vivid memories.

In the foreground a toy dog on wheels stands on the garden path. Attached to his hind quarters is a handle, at the perfect height for me to push him forward. It seems I've parked him for a moment because I need to tell him something important. The photograph shows me, crouching down, in the easy way small children do, so I can meet his glassy, brown stare and deliver my message. Looking on in the background are Mum's Aunt Becky and Uncle Jack, my Nanna and Poppa, smiling from their striped canvas deck chairs. The sort you used to see on the beach or the pier of British seaside towns. My parents always used deck chairs in the garden. This was a simpler time, long before garden centres and DIY superstores put the idea of chic outdoor furniture into people's heads.

My dad would have taken this photograph with his Kodak Box Brownie camera, holding it in that weird way at stomach height, to better align the image in the viewfinder. Mum's not in the frame. She would probably have been inside, restoring the kitchen to perfection. In the photo, the sun shines on Nanna's white hair. Perhaps it was a Bank Holiday outing and they came on the train, all the way from Stoke Newington to witness this moment. I'm a winter baby so it couldn't have been my birthday.

I have no specific memory of the actual day, though there is something familiar about the toy dog. It's Nanna's hair that brings to the surface another buried memory. A grieving mind plays strange tricks. My adult life evaporates and I'm small again. There's a shiver, a shudder and then tears. It was that time when Mum left me with Nanna for lunch. Everyone knew I was a fussy eater.

An old baggy cushion had been taken from the armchair by the fire, plumped up and placed on a rickety wooden chair for me to sit at the table. I remember how crackly static made the material attach itself to the back of my legs, and the fusty, dusty smell it released as the depleted stuffing collapsed beneath me. A cloth bib was tied around my neck and there was a silent pause while Nanna mashed a knob of soft yellow butter into a mushy white substance, on a white enamel plate with a black rim. Steam rose in clouds from the plate.

She sat beside me to explain and persuade, cajoling me to look at the lovely lunch she's made for me. There was a smell coming from it that I didn't like, so I shook my head and kept my mouth firmly closed. She put down the battered fork she used for the mashing and took up a teaspoon. Some of the white stuff clung to the fork and a small blob dropped onto the plastic tablecloth. She didn't notice but the tiny mess bothered me. When the butter was just a glistening smudge on the surface, she took up a teaspoon of

11

the mixture, blowing on it to cool it down, before bringing it towards my closed mouth. I looked at Nanna's white hair and then at my white lunch on the white plate with a black rim. It was the butter that fooled me.

"Lovely mashed 'tato, darlin'. Open wide like a good girl, for Nanna," she said, opening her mouth to show me what to do. Without thinking I copied her. In it went, but oh it wasn't what she said at all! An unexpected taste and an unfamiliar flaky texture on my tongue made me shiver. It all happened so fast, and without meaning to I swallowed the mouthful she got past me, before crying out all the complicated feelings that a small child cannot express in any other way. She said it was mashed potato. She knew it was horrible, steamed white fish but pretended it was potato to trick me into eating something that was good for me. Why did Mum let her do that? Why did she leave me here? Where did she go?

Startled by the ferocity of my anger, I return the photo to its correct folder, and choose another.

In my hand is a black and white image of a different child, from another time. Aged about three, she's pictured sitting on a little stool, holding what looks to be a posy of flowers. Her dark hair tumbles in beautifully arranged ringlets to her shoulders. Her embroidered dress is pristine, her tiny shoes look new. There's no one else in the frame except this sad little doll with my mother's face, the child, and the adult she became, alarmingly captured in a single shot.

It's a photograph I've seen before. Then, as now, I find it unsettling. I think back to the conversation we had when I saw it for the first time.

12

"You look unhappy. I can see it in your eyes."

Taking the photo from me, she stared at herself, frozen in black and white time, all those years ago.

"I look like I'm missing something," she concluded, handing the photograph back to me.

To me, the child in the photograph appears to be looking far beyond the camera's lens, beyond the person taking the photograph. A lonely little girl, looking for *someone* she can't quite see. A little girl, looking for her mother, somewhere over the rainbow. I put the picture back and that's when I find one I've never seen before.

Tucked away, behind the old holiday snaps and more recent photographs of her grandchildren is a larger, professional head and shoulders portrait of a beautiful young woman in black chiffon and pearls, looking straight into the camera. The hint of a smile plays around her mouth and her wavy bobbed hair suggests 1920s glamour. A wow photograph, that couldn't fail to make an impression on the viewer. I turn it over, hoping a date has been recorded that will confirm the era and give a clue to the woman's identity. No date, but in Mum's familiar handwriting, it simply says, *'My Mother'*. Suspended in black and white time, a century ago, the clear gaze of a woman in her early twenties, looks, with hope towards her future and ours. Her eyes and mouth are strangely like my own. The grandmother that never was.

3

North London, 1960s

When I look through my memory mirror at my eight-year-old self I see a child with sad blue eyes, looking out on her little girl's world through thick blue spectacles. Her light brown hair is held in a neat ponytail with a thick rubber band, disguised by a blue checked ribbon. A shy, bookish girl with her father's round face, a child that watches and listens to the adults.

Mum described me as aloof and she made it sound a thoroughly undesirable thing to be. I'm sure she would have preferred a more demonstrative, openly affectionate child, but she was stuck with an observer and a thinker. Sometimes my thoughts made tears come but I wasn't always unhappy, although people kept telling me I was.

'Cheer up, it might never happen', was a phrase that random strangers often threw in my direction. My soft little heart grew a little harder every time a bus conductor or a shop assistant took aim; their reward, my barely concealed anger.

On the day of the school prize-giving my parents took me out for tea and cakes in our town's only department store. The elderly waitress with a tight perm adjusted her white apron and headed to our table, noting me, the unsmiling, chubby girl, wearing the peculiar brown and yellow uniform of Peterborough and St Margaret's High School for Girls. Spoilt and over-indulged said her pinched mouth. Maybe I was a little....by Dad.

Whenever I was ill and had to stay in bed Dad would come home with a book for me. The last time, when I had measles, he bought a story with my name in the title, as if it had been written just for me. He knew I loved books.

I had a new, hard bound copy of *A Christmas Carol* in my leather satchel. Afternoon tea was a treat for winning another prize. I wished we could just go straight home so I could start reading and not have to talk. It must have been my demeanour that prompted an unexpected question, casually dropped into the air as the tea was being poured.

"Are you worried about anything?" from Dad.

Two concerned faces. Scarcely a beat.

"No. Can I have some cake please?"

Dad made eye contact with Mum, the merest flicker of an eyebrow indicating that the question had been asked and a satisfactory answer received. Dad wasn't the type to go looking for trouble.

There *was* something, but I couldn't find the words to explain, even if I wanted to, which I didn't then. I didn't even recognise it as a worry. It was more like a heavy uncomfortable feeling, like a pain in the place where I though my stomach might be, a tight feeling in my head, and not being able to swallow. It happened that time in the car on the way to see our relatives.

It was a grey Saturday afternoon and we were whirring through the London suburbs in Dad's Vauxhall Victor, a familiar journey we did at least once a month. I was silent in the back, listening to my own thoughts and trying to block out Mum's seething discontent in the front.

The combined smell of *Coty L'aimant* perfume and hair lacquer was overwhelming as usual. Opening a window was not allowed, unless I was going to be sick which never happened. Dad passed me his crumpled white handkerchief, just in case, but I put it on the shelf behind me.

The merest hint of moving air in the car could never be tolerated for fear it would compromise the achievements of the *Elnett* spray and its suffocating, extra hold mist. Our house was also a sealed unit because Mum said opening windows made the net curtains grubby with dust and let in dirt-loving insects.

We stopped at some traffic lights and with the engine idling I stared at the passengers in the back seat of the car next to ours. A boy and a girl, about my age were chattering, laughing and bouncing up and down on their seats. Their mum in the front, turned to share a joke. The boy suddenly looked across and smiled at me through the window. I stuck out my tongue and turned away just as the lights changed and the Vauxhall jerked forward.

I imagined him telling his side of the story.

'Mum, a girl in that white car with the red roof just stuck out her tongue at me'.

He'd probably be pointing in the direction of our car and his voice would have a 'that's not fair' whine to it.

I looked through the back window, watched the car take a left turn and slip out of sight. The realisation that I could be naughty without consequences was delicious.

16

My mother wasn't the kind that other people had, one that played games with you during car journeys. She was the needy one in our family, the one whose mood could suddenly change, the one that must be considered, deferred to and placated or else Dad would get a tongue lashing. I hated her for that and the way she held on to her simmering anger and resentment like a weapon, always ready to be reloaded and discharged. I often thought there must be something wrong with me for having those feelings.

Before we left the house today I heard her tell Dad he drove her mad with his timekeeping. I heard him remind her of the need to get ready when she hadn't yet completed her polishing and tidying rituals, and she must have noticed him looking at his watch. That would be the reason for the tense atmosphere in the car and the gesture of displeasure which was my mother's trademark. A slow look at the offending party, then the eyelids closing in contempt before the final defiant toss and turn of the head, followed by a long gaze out of the passenger window. When I saw her do that the heavy feeling started in my stomach and moved to my head. Dad tried to smooth it all over before we arrived at Grandma's flat, but it didn't work. Mum called it *schmoozing*.

"Don't start schmoozing me, just because you're frightened of your mother. She won't die if we're a few minutes late," she snapped.

I could see the top half of Dad's face in the driver's mirror. He did a strange sort of blink with his whole face when he heard that comment.

17

The first stop was near Tavistock Square and when we arrived Dad parked the car close to a large block of 1930s studio flats with a smart name and a lift to the different floors, like in the department stores. When the button was pressed the mechanism always let out a 'thunk' before descending. A black metal gate was pulled across before we stepped in and then had to be clanked shut again before it took us up to the sixth floor. In the short walk from the lift we passed nine identical wooden doors. The smell in the corridor was always the same: recently cooked lunches, mixed with underlying notes of mothballs.

In the lift I thought about my grandma in the one-person kitchen, buttering slices of caraway loaf and placing a teaspoon in the china bowl for the blackcurrant jam, while the clock with the thick black numbers tick-tocked on the wall above the kitchen door.

I wondered if she was looking at the clock and tut-tutting to herself because we said three and it had gone quarter past. The white linen tablecloth had probably been on the dining table since noon and the cake, from her favourite baker's shop near St Pancras, would have been placed in position, ready for our arrival.

We rat-a-ta-tatted on her metal letterbox and we heard her say to herself, "Ah, they're here." A few seconds later the door opened and there she was, greeting us with an indulgent smile.

Grandma had grey hair and lines around her eyes, but she was steady on her feet and didn't wear glasses or false teeth. Her hands looked much older than the rest of her because her fingers were bent into a strange shape.

"You're later than you said. You should know what the traffic's like on a Saturday." She scanned Dad's face for a response as we all filed in behind him.

"Never mind, we're here now," said Dad, bending to kiss his mother on her cheek. I followed behind and planted mine in the same spot.

"What a big girl you're getting," she said to me and then to Mum, "She's filling out now, isn't she, Sylvia?"

"Hello, Mum. Yes, well, it's about time. She's the image of Ida, don't you think?"

I wondered why Mum always called Grandma 'Mum' because she is Dad's mum, not hers.

I kept hearing that I looked like my Auntie Ida, Dad's sister who lived in New Zealand. She came over here when I was just a baby, so I don't remember her at all. New Zealand sounded a long way away, but I planned to go there and visit her myself when I was older.

Mum kissed Grandma too, but I could tell she didn't really want to because her face wasn't smiling like Dad's.

Uncle Bernard, the eldest of Grandma's children, was going to join us for tea. He lived in the flat opposite, so he could look after Grandma. No one ever said this, but I thought that it was really the other way around. Uncle Bernard had never married and still needed his mum even though he was about sixty years old.

Grandma went to the kitchen to fill the teapot and asked Dad to nip across the hall to tell Uncle Bernard to join us.

Mum was seated, legs crossed in the black wooden chair with the wicker back, gazing out of the window with a bored look. She patted the back of her hair to make sure everything was still in place.

"Do you want me to carry the pot in?" she called from the chair, but Grandma said she could manage.

I didn't feel like sitting so I stood in my favourite spot, in front of the wooden corner cabinet with the glass door, where all Grandma's treasures were stored. On the middle shelf two rectangular silver dishes with matching lids stood on both sides, with a row of crystal glasses positioned between them. I started counting the glasses, but then Uncle Bernard came bounding in with Dad following in his wake.

"Well, well, what have we here? Ahem, good afternoon, good afternoon."

Uncle Bernard struck a pose in the middle of the room, one hand behind his back, the other extended towards Mum who remained seated. Bowing his head, he took a step closer, so she could take his proffered hand.

Mum had seen this act before and looked unimpressed with the formal handshake but took his hand anyway. He clicked his heels together before turning to me, hand outstretched.

"And a very good afternoon to you, young lady."

I laughed and played the game too.

"No kissing. I don't do kissing," he muttered, taking his place in his usual spot at the head of the table. When he sat down it was our signal to do the same.

"Now, I want to hear all about school. How's she doing Leslie?" He bellowed the question at Dad, looking from him to Mum as if his life depended on receiving an immediate and positive answer.

"An excellent report and a prize," said Dad, willing me to share the good news.

Grandma gave a nod of approval in my direction, urging me to elaborate.

"I won the prize for English composition," I managed, grateful that my time to get a word in was probably limited.

There was an audible 'ah' of approval from Grandma and Uncle Bernard leaned forward in his chair, eyes wide at this news. He had very pretty, green eyes for a man, with thick, dark lashes giving him the look of a silent movie star.

"Composition, eh? Ve-rr-ee good. Very good indeed. I'm pleased to hear that. Oh, yes. Composition. Runs in the family, of course. Stands to reason. Writing. In the blood."

He sat back in his chair, still nodding and repeating these thoughts to himself as Grandma poured the tea and passed him a cup. A bowl of white sugar cubes with a pair of silver tongs was placed within his reach. When he dropped two cubes into his tea a tiny splash landed on the back of his hand, but he didn't notice.

"English was always my best subject at school," said Mum, attempting to enter the conversation, but Uncle Bernard was about to launch into one of his favourite topics; the proven writing talent on his side of the family. I was interested in hearing more about this, so I wanted him to continue. Meanwhile Grandma was signalling at me with a misshapen finger to take more bread and butter and for Dad to cut the cake.

"The Kersh brothers. That's where she gets it from. One a Fleet Street newspaper editor and his brother, a genius of a novelist. Both in the family! Our cousins! Talent, y'see. Always finds a way through," he said.

21

Everyone laughed, more at the delivery than the content.

There's some more conversation about the genius novelist also being a *meshuggeneh* which means a crazy person. Then the adults talked about other, less interesting people in the family for a bit until it was time to say goodbye and we had to go through all the coming-in rituals in reverse, with Uncle Bernard holding out his hand and repeating the mantra that no kissing was required in his case.

Across town, in much less well to-do Stoke Newington, Mum's Uncle Jack, Aunt Becky and Becky's unmarried sister Clara, were waiting for us to arrive. Another car ride brought us to their house, where four uneven concrete steps led to a battered front door with etched glass panels.

There was a vertical line of doorbells with different names on them. Mum selected the one at the bottom and we waited for Becky or Nanna, as I called her, to let us in. It was raining, and Mum was worrying about what would happen to her hair if Nanna kept us waiting on the step much longer. She seemed more relaxed though because this was her family and she didn't have to watch her Ps and Qs with them. Finally, we made out Nanna's shape and the flowered pattern of her apron through the misty glass. She didn't have many teeth, so her smile seemed to push her face into a strange shape.

"Come in outa the cold," she said, hurrying us in. "You'll catch yer death at the finish, standing out there in this."

"You're telling me," said Mum. "How are you?"

The stress was on the 'are' and her tone sounded flat as if she wasn't really interested in the reply.

"Not bad. Clara drives me mad. Gives me 'eadache." She broke off when she saw me walking in behind Mum, put both her hands round my face and pinched my cheeks.

"Look at 'er face! Those cheeks! Growing tall, ain't she, Sylv?" "Shootin up, you are!" she said to me, still gripping my face in her cold hands.

I wanted her to let go. Luckily, Dad provided the next distraction and she released her grip.

"Oh, Les! Jack's been waiting for yer to come. 'E's having trouble with a light bulb." She looked at my dad as if he was a saviour, with the power to right everything wrong in her world.

We followed her along a narrow, chilly corridor, past the front parlour, which I'd only been in once. Ahead, the stairs led up to a mysterious, musty unknown where other people lived, but we always went downstairs into a sitting room, dominated by a table covered with a plastic cloth. A couple of mismatched armchairs were arranged there on either side of an open fire. Gentle Jack, the man I called Poppa, was seated at the table watching a wrestling match on television with the sound turned off. Auntie Clara, with her shaky hands and high-pitched whispery voice, rose from her place at the fireside to greet us. Our arrival was the highlight of everyone's day, and it must have also offered them some respite from each other.

Poppa reached out to take Dad's hand, his face a picture of gratitude that help had arrived.

"Hello Jack," Dad said, "where's this light you want help with then?"

"I'll show ya, Les. 'Arf a mo', lemme get up an' say 'ello properly."

23

He placed a large hand on the table to take his great weight and once upright and steady he looked at Mum. An arm went around her shoulder and they kissed each other on the cheek. I saw her wink and press a five-pound note into his hand before he slowly bent to stroke the top of my head with his other hand.

Then he made his way back up the stairs to the bedroom, with Dad following behind to attend to the faulty light. Poppa was wide and his legs bowed under his weight. He rocked from side to side when he walked, as if alternating the load bearing was the only way his curved limbs could continue to propel him forward.

It was Auntie Clara's turn to cup my face in her hands, smiling at me in wonderment whilst remarking on my great height. Her cheeks were always rosy red but today they looked burnt, as if she'd been sitting by the fireside for too long. I was sure I was quite small for my age, but all my relatives seemed to think I was very tall. Mum and Nanna were warming their hands by the fire.

"Ain't she gorgeous, Rose?" Clara said to Mum, and then to me, "Auntie Clara's got something for you, darlin'. Come with me an' I'll show yer'," she whispered, finally releasing my face so I could move off the spot.

Auntie Clara always called Mum, 'Rose'. Like a nickname I suppose.

Nanna looked up just as I was being led, willingly, out of the sitting room and spoke sharply.

"Clara, where're you taking her? Don't *schlep* her up to your room now. She don't need that. Sit down. I'm fetching the tea up."

To make the tea, Nanna disappeared underground, or so it appeared to me, for this was a Victorian terrace with a scarily dark cellar and beyond this, a scullery. I went down there once and saw a small opening, high up on the back wall of the cellar. By this little patch of light, the black, misshapen monster that lived down there transformed itself into an enormous pile of coal.

Clara didn't pay any attention to Nanna, so I followed behind. I'd done this once before and when we got to her room she did something very surprising. I was anticipating a repeat performance.

Clara's room was freezing cold after the warmth of the fire, but I didn't mind because just like the last time, she was bending herself into an unnatural position by the empty fireplace with one arm reaching up the chimney.

She hid her red leather purse up there and it was probably a secret that only I knew about. I was sure Nanna would have told her off if she'd found out. Clara was very old but her rosy cheeks, tiny voice and familiarity with the interior of chimneys were fairy-like to me.

I said thank you for the half-crown she gave me, putting it safely in the pocket of my dress while she returned the purse to its hiding place.

There was a bathroom at Grandma's flat but at the Stoke Newington house, there was just an outside toilet in the back yard. At the time I didn't think about how they washed themselves. They might have had a tin bath or perhaps they paid tuppence for a tub of hot water, a small piece of soap and a scratchy towel at the public baths. In between times, they must have managed with what Mum called a 'cat's lick' at the sink.

Back downstairs Clara insisted on helping Nanna bring the cups of tea from the kitchen to the table, despite her shaking hands. The rattle of the approaching crockery indicated the tea

25

was slurping into the saucers, so Dad leaped up to help. Undeterred Clara returned to collect the next cup.

"For gawd's sake SIT DOWN," said Nanna. "It'll all go on the floor at the finish. *Oy vay*, she'll put me in an early grave, that one, she will."

"You're right there," added Poppa, with a contemptuous look in Clara's direction.

I felt sorry for Clara because they were so harsh, but she took absolutely no notice of them.

"Leave her alone, she's trying to help you," said Mum. "Come on, Clara, let me take it now. You sit down and have yours."

Clara looked up, as if hearing Mum's voice had broken her concentration on the task in hand. "You got yourn, Rose? Hold my cup, a minute while I sit down then," she said. Auntie Clara always said 'yourn' when she meant 'yours'.

Nanna liked everyone to eat and we all managed some of the apple pie she'd made, even though we were still full, from Grandma's cake. I liked the way she put sultanas in with the apples and sprinkled lots of sugar on top of the pastry.

Then Dad remembered the fried fish we brought with us was still in the car. He brought in the foil package and a jar of purple *chrain* for them to eat with it. I tried this once, but the horseradish that went in with the grated beetroot hurt the inside of my nose. Dad said I might like it better when I'm older.

Nanna collected sixpences and threepenny bits to give to me. Before we said goodbye and I was told to give everyone a kiss, a little stack of coins was pressed into my expectant hands, together with a bar of *Fry's Chocolate Cream* and a tube of *Smarties*.

Mum and Poppa gave each other a hug before we left, and I heard her say to him, "God bless, and look after yourself."

Both sides of my family were Jewish, but they were worlds apart. None of them were very religious but they sometimes used different words and names for things that I only heard other Jewish people use.

Auntie Clara was the only one that always called Mum 'Rose', though. Everyone else called her Sylvia. Rose was her middle name. Maybe it would have hurt Clara's feelings too much and made her feel silly if that mistake was mentioned as well. That must be why no one ever said anything about it.

In the car on the way home I secretly counted my coins, wondering if the sixpences on their own were enough to buy a book. I could save the half-crown and the threepenny bits for something else.

4

The next week, Mum was cleaning the upstairs hall. "He's left late this morning. Maybe he does shifts at the weekend." She was half talking to Dad, but mostly thinking out loud, while she dusted.

We could see the comings and goings next door from our upstairs hall window, so Mum saw Mr Hewson drive off. He was a policeman and he often chatted to Dad on a Sunday while they were both washing their cars in the driveway.

The Hewson's had four children, two boys and a girl that were older than me, and another girl called Susan, nearer my age. I often wanted to play with Susan, but it was never easy because our mums didn't like each other.

A couple of weeks ago there'd been a bit of a commotion at the Hewson's house and I could hear Mum and Dad discussing it in the kitchen.

"She's got a cheek. The way she looks me up and down, after what went on the other night," said Mum with a sniff of disapproval.

"It's him I feel sorry for," said Dad. "It can't be easy with his job, if one of his kids gets into trouble. It took both of us to hold that son of his back the other night. He was still shouting and swearing after he'd kicked a hole in their back door."

There was a pause before I heard Mum respond.

"It's very awkward for me when you speak to him. Then I feel obliged to make conversation with *her*. Just because she's married to a policeman she thinks that makes her someone. I've seen her looking down her nose. Now she'll be embarrassed when she sees me because I know what's gone on. I know her type."

"Whatever her faults you can't say she didn't act promptly when you had the accident," said Dad.

"That was different," said Mum. "Anyone would have called an ambulance when they saw the amount of blood in the kitchen that day."

"God knows what would have happened if she hadn't been in that afternoon," said Dad, collecting his coat from the hook in the hall. "I had the fright of my life when I got that call from the hospital. I couldn't thank her enough really."

Mum had a scar on her left wrist from an accident that happened when she was reaching up to clean the shelf above the fridge. Glass tumblers stacked inside each other fell out of her hand when she lost her footing on the chair she was standing on. One of them shattered when it hit the top of the fridge and a piece of glass pierced the skin inside her wrist, just where the blue green veins criss-cross under the skin.

That's what I heard the adults say happened anyway. I was playing in my room when I heard a glass smash and then Mum shouted for me to run next door and fetch Mrs Hewson.

Mrs Hewson told me to stay at her house with Susan and together we saw an ambulance coming up the street with its lights flashing. I saw Mum being lifted into the ambulance on a sort of chair. It looked like she had a tea towel round one wrist. Mrs

Hewson came back and said not to worry, they were taking Mum to hospital and my dad was coming back from work early to get me.

I listened to them going over it in the kitchen below.

"I must have passed out. When I woke up a doctor was standing over me saying I'd lost a lot of blood. I thought I was there because I'd had a miscarriage. Bought it all back. So, funny how your mind works," said Mum with a funny vibration in her voice.

"They told you to take it easy," Dad said. "Why won't you listen?"

"Well, you know me. I can't take it easy with a house to keep clean. Some women might be able to sit back and watch the dust pile up, but I'm not one of them."

"I know," said Dad with a sigh. "See you later, I'd better get off."

He called goodbye up the stairs but didn't hear me reply because just at that moment Mum pressed her foot on the power button to start vacuuming. The familiar ebb and flow of the motor's roar floated up the stairs as she went back and forth across the dark red carpet.

I waited until she switched it off and the machine had been returned to the cupboard under the stairs before I came downstairs.

"I've finished my jobs, so when I've got my face on, we'll get the bus into town," she said to the hall mirror.

I was glad we were going into town. Going shopping with Mum meant I could, 'accidently on purpose' forget about practising the piano.

I could never seem to play the scales without a making a mistake. It felt so lonely doing it all by myself in an empty room. I always seemed to press down on the wrong keys and those sounds got mixed up with the phone ringing in the hall. It made my fingers wobble and then I played the wrong notes again. I hated it all and sometimes I wanted to slam the lid of the piano down hard until all the keys were smashed and all the sounds were silenced.

I had my coat on ready to go. We'd have time to go to the bookshop and Mum said I could choose something.

When we left the house, Mrs Hewson was digging in her front garden. She looked up when Mum closed the front door and adjusted the frilly pinny tied round her waist. An auburn curl had fallen forward, across her spectacles, and she used the back of her hand to brush it away.

"Alright?" she said to Mum, her mouth staying in a tight little line.

"O, hell-low. Everything settled down now, has it?" This was the refined voice Mum used when she wanted to impress people on the telephone and sometimes in person too.

"Yes, thank you. Off out, somewhere nice, are we?"

She eyed the collar of Mum's red leather coat, whilst ever so slightly altering her position to get a better look at Mum's black patent leather shoes. I knew Mum had noticed this too. I felt her bristling beside me, and her reply was designed to tantalise.

"Just a few things to do in town." And to me, she said, "Come along, we don't want to miss the bus." She said, 'in town', as if the local high street was the West End and we were going there to spend, spend, spend.

As we made our way up the street, Mum's high heels tip-tapped defiantly on the pavement. At the corner, I glanced back. Mrs Hewson, arms folded across her body, was staring in our direction. Mum didn't look back.

5

Mum's strategy for keeping her domestic world in order involved a strict, but predictable regime of household tasks that could not be altered, curtailed or postponed. She called it being house proud.

She claimed to love housework but it made her miserable and bad-tempered all the same. The pleasure lay not in the doing but in the completion, when all evidence that we actually lived in our three-bed semi had been purged from every room.

All through my childhood and during pregnancy she kept a relentless hold on the domestic chores. After my brother was born she resumed her part-time job, baulking at any suggestion of hired help. The idea of handing such a responsibility to another woman was a non-starter. I still marvel at how she managed to keep us all in clean clothes with only a line in the garden, *Lux* soap flakes and the kitchen sink. A boiler which needed frequent feeding with coke was also a messy business. The mania she had for cleaning wasn't helped by the fact that it was such a hard slog to simply stay on top of it all. We had a ceiling airer on a pulley system and all the ironing was done at the kitchen table, covered in a thick sheet for the purpose. A laundry van collected bedclothes and nappies and the dry cleaners was also called into service for the good clothes.

In addition to the daily washing, dusting and vacuuming duties, every couple of months I would discover her bending low or climbing high in a bid to access all parts of the hard-to-reach places in our home.

On those days I watched her disappear away from me, searching for Narnia in the cupboard under the stairs, dustpan and brush in hand. Or balanced on a chair at the bay window of the lounge, so the net curtains could be removed for another hand wash they didn't need. The room faced onto the street so when all six curtains were down we were exposed to the full gaze of the world for the next twenty-four hours.

Often, I'd be drawing at the kitchen table as the cleaning continued around me. Installed at some height, the kitchen cupboards were an ever-present, looming threat, for in her mind these harboured unseen layers of dirt that must be routinely flushed out. A bowl of hot soapy water would be placed on the kitchen table and then began a procession of tins and packets downward to any available surface. Cloth in hand, back up she'd go to wash and wipe the interior surfaces clean of the grime she believed was there.

The food shopping and cooking duties were taken care of by Dad who was a professional chef, but the organisation and storage of tinned and dry goods came under Mum's jurisdiction. When Dad needed anything from above, it was Mum, the keeper of the cupboards, who insisted on rising to locate the chosen item, passing it down like a museum curator handling a priceless exhibit.

According to Mum, dust and dirt, if left to settle on a surface, encouraged the advance of ants, mice and spiders. I was told these pests were particularly attracted to pencil sharpenings, so I was not allowed to carry out this maintenance in my bedroom, unsupervised. All pencils had to be sharpened straight into the kitchen bin under Mum's watchful eye, lest a stray shaving escape my attention and land on the floor.

Mum started her daily routine upstairs with a polishing challenge she was devoted to. The new wardrobes that dominated one wall of my parents' bedroom had doors with a high gloss beige finish and every day she checked every inch of the surface for stray finger marks. The doors had no handles and shut with a click. They were impossible to open without leaving tell-tale evidence of human interference that had to be removed daily. She also spent a lot of time arranging and rearranging her clothes, carefully angling each garment on its identical hanger, lest it should make contact with its neighbour, thus causing a crease of disapproval that would necessitate the exercise being repeated again and again. This kind of wardrobe maintenance was usually the prelude to an evening spent trying on outfits in front of the mirror. My parents had been invited to a wedding and Mum was in two minds about wearing a long evening gown. The garment in question had been hung on the back of the bedroom door, as a reminder that a decision needed to be made.

That evening she tried it on and had a practice run. She was petite and the clingy, crepe fabric with a dramatic off-the-shoulder neckline swamped her little frame. I was sitting on the bedroom floor with a book, but I stopped reading when she started applying her make-up because I liked watching what she did.

She had a collection of Max Factor pencils, pots and palettes to create the Elizabeth Taylor look. A thick wedge of black colour was applied close to the upper lash line and then, using her finger, a jade coloured cream was rubbed across the rest of the lid. Black mascara in a small dry block came with an applicator resembling a tiny toothbrush. It all seemed most unpromising until she brought it to life with a bit of spit. The brush was then wiped across the moistened block to transfer enough of the boot black colour onto the brush. With her mouth peculiarly ajar, she stared into the mirror, tilting her head to ensure the brush hit its target every time.

She slipped her feet into a pair of silver stiletto heels and the transformation was complete. After a last look in the mirror she went downstairs. When the third stair from the bottom creaked beneath her foot I took my book and followed her downstairs.

She sashayed into the kitchen and took up a position in front of the sink, with one foot turned demurely out, like a model posing for a photograph. Dad was reading his newspaper. He didn't look up straightaway.

"Put that paper down a minute. I want you to look at me in this and tell me what you think."

I knew she wanted Dad to tell her that she looked a million dollars, that she was the most glamorous, stylish, beautiful woman he had ever seen. He was kind, but he didn't say any of those things.

''Oh! Right. Very nice. Turn around. It's an unusual colour, isn't it?" Dad was colour blind, so he was already straying into dangerous territory, guaranteed to rile.

"Unusual colour? What are you talking about? It's classic French navy! Unusual, he says!" Mum often called on an invisible third person for impact but oblivious, Dad blundered on.

"Oh, navy, is it? You know I'm no good with colours. It looks sort of brown to me."

"Why do you always have to focus on the wrong thing? Never mind the colour – what about the style?"

"Well it's very smart for the wedding. Flattering, really."

"What do you mean, flattering?"

Dad started to flounder. "Well I, err... it suits you!"

"You didn't say that the last time I wore it?"

"I don't remember seeing you in it before."

"Oh, for goodness sake! I've worn it a million times. That's it, it's going. I can tell you think it's frumpy."

"When did I say that? Frumpy hasn't passed my lips."

"You didn't have to. It's that look on your face!"

He chuckled at the accusation, trying to encourage her to see the funny side of his hopeless predicament. "What look have I got? I haven't got any look. You're mad!"

There was no way back now and so she flounced out, vowing never to ask his opinion again. He called up from the bottom of the stairs. "The dress looks lovely. What do you want me to say?"

"Nothing! Nothing at all. I'm sorry I asked."

Dad's slippers swished on the carpet as he trudged back to the kitchen. The sound of his feet made me think he was sad because of what Mum had said.

Sometimes she let me have her reject dresses for dressing up so I followed her upstairs to the bedroom but there was something else I needed to ask first. She was putting the evening shoes back in their allotted space at the bottom of the wardrobe.

"Mum, why has Dad got a mum, but Nanna and Poppa are your aunt and uncle?"

She looked up when she heard the question and her face still looked cross from the conversation with Dad. "Well, because Nanna and Poppa are like a mum and dad. They adopted me when I was a little girl. It's time you got ready for bed."

I wondered what it would be like to be adopted. I didn't connect it with loss or sadness. Being adopted sounded interesting and special, like an unexpected discovery or a nice surprise. No further explanation was needed because my imagination train had left the station.

What if I didn't really belong to this family? Maybe my 'real' parents will come here one day to take me back? It was an exciting idea, but I kept my thoughts to myself because it would make Mum angry if she knew what I was thinking. I knew that every family was different, and everyone else's seemed much more interesting than mine.

I'd already had a glimpse of the kind of girl I could be with different parents and an older sibling, because of Jacqueline Muir and her family.

Jacqueline was a couple of years older than me and she was like a big sister. We went to the same school and travelled on the bus together on the days Mum went to work. It suited Mum that someone else could look after me when she was busy, so I spent a lot of time at Jacqueline's house and her set-up was not at all like mine.

Jacqueline's parents were Scottish, spoke with a strange accent and were much older than my parents. Her dad spent most of his time at home, painting pictures and looking after his bees. He used to work in China when he was younger and had a lot of special Chinese ornaments that he kept in a locked display case in his study. He didn't mind us looking at them through the glass.

There was an apple orchard at the bottom of their garden to play in and a clearing where the bees were kept. We kept a safe distance from the beehives when we saw Mr Muir collecting the honey, in his white clothes, wearing a funny hat with a veil covering his face. I didn't want to spread something on my toast that was made by bees, but I thought Mr Muir was very brave to put himself in danger from all their buzzing to get it.

An ancient grandfather clock constantly bing-bonged in the hallway of their house and there was always a distinctly doggy aroma there, from Honey, their long-haired cocker spaniel. Mrs Muir didn't seem to care about the rain spoiling her hair or whether the house was in a mess. Piles of books, papers and ornaments covered every surface so that cleaning must have been hard to do, but Mrs Muir never gave any indication that this was something she was concerned about. I couldn't imagine her ever wearing an evening dress or getting annoyed if Mr Muir said the wrong thing about her clothes.

I was a little frightened of Mrs Muir until I got used to her accent. She was often in the kitchen, preparing dishes that sounded grown-up and tasted delicious, like Welsh Rarebit. The family made a point of watching any particularly Scottish programmes on television, like the *White Heather Club* and Mr Muir sometimes wore a kilt. There was another peculiar animal smell in the house whenever Mrs Muir cooked haggis. The children could taste it if they wanted to but when I found out it was a stuffed sheep's stomach I said no thank you.

Downstairs, in the back room of the house, there was a big old piano. Jacqueline had a lesson every week and her music books were kept in an untidy pile on the top. She showed me how to play a tune called *Chopsticks* that used the black keys and the yellowy coloured ones. We both sat on the piano stool and she played her bit and I played mine and it sounded like a proper piece of music. When Dad came to pick me up, we played it again for him, and he thought it was very good.

They had an extra room in the attic of their house where we played board games or listened to records. We liked the funny stories told by a man with an American accent called Bob Newhart. We had to climb up a stepladder to reach the small opening at the top but there was enough room for a few of us to be up there at the same time, all giggling and having fun.

One year I even had my birthday party at Jacqueline's house. Mum probably thought it would make too much mess to have lots of children tramping through our lounge and since she was pregnant with my brother, Mrs Muir must have offered to help out. I don't remember a single time that Jacqueline came to my house to play, although one summer she did come with us on a holiday to France. We kept count of the number of *Coca-Colas* we drank in two weeks. It was well into the twenties.

A few days after the incident with the evening dress I went to their house and her mum said I could play upstairs in Jacqueline's bedroom until she came back from her piano lesson.

I sat on the bed and wondered how I could amuse myself. There was an old-fashioned wardrobe made of heavy dark wood in one corner of the room. A door had swung open and some of the drawers inside were half-closed as if someone had been in too much of a hurry to care how they were left. I recognised the dressing up clothes, spilling out from some of them.

I started at the top drawer and worked down, depositing everything I found in each one on the bed. There was a pile of hats, long flowing skirts, dolls clothes, swathes of tartan fabric, chiffon scarves, richly coloured velvet dresses and a poncho. All the clothes had a musty, old smell about them. Mixed up with them was a funny false beard, some random playing cards, a book of magic tricks, bits of stage makeup, homemade masks, several curly wigs, a cape, a couple of old blankets and a set of oil paints.

I remained focused on creating my own order out of the chaos. I folded all the clothes neatly and put each item back separately. I stored the disparate accessories and objects together, making sure each drawer could close without hindrance, as it was supposed to do. Some of the drawers were stiff and went back in a crooked way and I had to try a few times before they closed properly. I put the blankets by themselves in the bottom drawer because they were for the bed and not part of the dressing up collection.

When I was satisfied that everything was as tidy as I liked my own toy cupboard to be at home, I sat back on my heels and smiled to myself, just as Mrs Muir put her head round the door and told me Jaqueline was home.

I didn't tell her what I'd done. I wanted my tidying up to be a big surprise for her. I was hoping she'd be so pleased she'd want to tell Mum what I did.

6

After Dad heard me playing *Chopsticks* with Jacqueline, he persuaded Mum that I had a musical talent that ought to be nurtured. In years to come she would recall this moment as proof that Dad's judgement was often a little awry.

"He came running in and said we have to get her a piano! He'd only heard you play tiddly, om, pom, pom! Talk about mad!" she said.

Whatever she might have thought later, once Dad put the piano idea in her head, Mum made sure it happened. She was never so happy as when she was planning to spend money and she immediately took charge of choosing the instrument. Dad couldn't be relied on, as in her view he invariably leaned towards the lowest cost.

Soon after we moved to the house where I would spend most of my childhood, I overheard them talking about knocking down part of the wall that separated the living room from the dining room.

"I'm not at all sure we need to knock it through, Sylvia," said Dad. "And I just can't picture what it will look like."

"Like Phyllis and Gerald have done with theirs," Mum replied. "It's called open plan. It's contemporary. Everyone's doing it. We don't need to knock the whole wall down. We could have an archway made."

It wasn't in my dad's nature to put up much of a fight about anything, so in accordance with Mum's vision, the separate spaces originally designated for 'dining' and 'living' became one. The room was renamed, 'the lounge' and in this new arrangement, an empty stretch of wall at one end could easily accommodate a moderately sized piano.

A strange kind of raised wall covering, designed to resemble a stone wall decorated the archway. Deliberate pretence in décor appealed to mum's taste. The material was reminiscent of grey cardboard egg boxes and if you pushed at the surface, to my horror, the impression you made with your finger, remained.

Then the furniture started to change. First to arrive were two curved settees, covered in a dark green *Dralon* fabric that wouldn't crease or crinkle when sat on, thus an ally in Mum's battle against any visible signs of use. In the window of the smart furniture store it appeared as one enormous half circle, but the space in our room wasn't big enough to accommodate such a dramatic statement piece, so to Mum's frustration it had to be displayed in less impressive quarters.

A glass topped dining table and six grey faux leather chairs with oval backs and no arm rests filled the bay window end. They were quite possibly the most uncomfortable dining chairs to ever grace a home, but I would not find this out for many years because nobody was ever allowed to use them. It was, like many aspects of our life, only for show. We ate all our meals at the blue *Formica* table in the kitchen.

The bay window of the lounge was dressed in a pair of floor length pinch-pleated orange drapes with tiebacks that hooked to the wall. These were never drawn at night because that would have altered the pleated lines and to open them would necessitate the material being coaxed back into its original position the next morning. As this feat could never be achieved to Mum's satisfaction, they always remained open. This was simply house law. It was like living in a pristine stage set. Everything was in position, but nothing was what it appeared to be.

At the opposite end of the room French windows opened onto a raised patio. These had only been opened once since we moved here, by the decorators. The lady of the house insisted they were closed before the white gloss paint was fully dry, thus ensuring they were sealed for all eternity, like all the other windows in the house.

In one corner of the dining area was a special piece of furniture that was all the rage. It was billed as a cocktail bar but was really nothing more than a glorified drinks cabinet without doors. A beckoning curved design featured a glass panel at the front to display the best glasses and a counter-top for the affable host to pour the requested drinks. On his side, open shelves housed the bottles of *Warnincks Advocaat,* sherry, vermouth, cherry brandy and whisky that we had. A few bottles of *Schweppes Bitter Lemon, Babycham* and a plastic ice bucket were stored there too.

Neither of my parents were big drinkers or entertainers. The only alcohol I ever saw Mum consume was at Christmas, when a *Peter Stuyvesant* cigarette was the accompaniment to a finger's width of whisky. Perched on the *Dralon,* with legs demurely crossed, she always made an elaborate show of not inhaling, her face disappearing behind clouds of smoke, until the puffs of grey fog made their way across the room like a spell of bad weather. At that time, the act of smoking was associated with film star glamour, so to me this annual indulgence was just another feature of my mother's extensive beauty repertoire.

In a setting that screamed suburban modernity, she was never going to give a second-hand 'old Joanna' house room. Oh no. We didn't even go to a shop for the purchase but drove to a piano factory where she selected a brand new upright mini pianoforte with a highly polished mahogany wood casing and matching stool. The cost must have been through the roof, but Dad just had to swallow it as it had been his idea in the first place.

Such a prestigious acquisition was her pride and joy. The sound of a bizarre scale echoed through our house when the duster made daily contact with all the keys from high to low. The piano soon had more attention from polishing than I gave it as a player.

As neither of my parents could play a musical instrument I felt the burden of expectation, but I knew I had no talent because nothing came easily or naturally to me. Lessons after school with a fusty, retired teacher were dull and practising the beginner's exercises was agony. Nothing sounded as good as *Chopsticks* with Jacqueline. Progressing to proper tunes and songs that anyone could recognise seemed a long way off. Especially so, during a school holiday, all those years ago when I was at home with Mum, trying to learn the scales.

The book was open on the piano stand. Reluctantly, I sat down and haltingly played the C scale, first with my right hand and then my left. Nearly right. Maybe I was improving. I repeated the exercise with each hand again to make sure it wasn't a fluke. Then I tried both hands together but just as I began, the phone rang and I lost my concentration. I'd have to try again. The phone was still ringing from the table in the hall, but I could hear Mum coming downstairs in some haste, so I returned to the task.

I was having trouble getting the fingers of my left hand in the correct position to hit the keys cleanly, and in the gaps in play I could hear Mum whispering. I couldn't make out what she was saying because she was also giggling. I didn't like the way it sounded. It went on and on, but I carried on with my scales, trying to block it out. Every time I went wrong and stopped, the noises from the hall were still going on. Eventually I played the scale right through with no stops, hitting the keys as hard as I could. I still made mistakes, but I didn't care. I just wanted to block out the telephone conversation.

My chest felt tight with anger and I banged both my hands down hard on the keys, again and again, producing the loudest, ugliest sound possible but nothing I did halted Mum's whispers and silly laughing.

Even at the age of eight I understood perfectly well that she was speaking to another man. One that made her laugh in that embarrassing, foolish sort of way, one that she said secret things to. I knew how she spoke to Dad and it wasn't anything like the noises I was hearing.

After this, the phone calls came on other days too but only when I was practising the piano. On too many mornings of that school holiday I sat at the piano, blinded by tears, unable to read the music I was supposed to be playing whilst the conversation carried on as if I didn't exist. I felt my heart beating in frustration and anger that I was party to a secret and a deceit that I didn't want to know anything about and was powerless to stop. The walls of my stage set lounge were wobbling around me.

One time I deliberately picked up the phone before Mum got to it, hoping that my intervention might somehow break the spell. I recited our number into the receiver but when I started to speak I heard a click and the line went dead.

"Who was that?"

"Don't know. There's no one there now."

"Must have been a wrong number."

She lingered close by, as if waiting for the caller to ring again. He did, and she picked up on the first ping.

What if I stopped practising the piano? I suspected that Mum gave the caller a two-ring signal that 'now' was a good time at her end. If I changed my routine, then maybe I could make it all go away.

The next morning, I stayed in my room and read my book. It was a faint hope that my action could work the required magic. From upstairs the familiar giggles intruded, dragging me back from an engrossing story to the horrible here and now. I read the same few lines several times over without comprehension and threw the book across the room.

The destructive feelings that this episode planted in me took root and mutated. Somewhere, deep inside my head it felt like my fault. The emotional landscape around me suddenly seemed too exposed and treacherous for an eight-year-old to be wandering about in. I wished I could just go to sleep and wake up as somebody else.

A few months later my piano teacher sent a report to my parents indicating that I was failing to make much progress. I overheard Mum tell Dad that practising every day seemed to have gone by the board since the school holidays and they were wasting money on lessons. A day or so later I asked Mum and Dad if I could stop having piano lessons and everyone agreed.

I didn't want to disappoint Dad by giving up on the piano but as Mum bought the new settees on hire purchase, maybe he was happy that I was saving him money elsewhere.

It transpired that it was a passing fancy and not a full-blown love affair. The phone calls eventually stopped, but I stayed watchful, suspicious and my mother's silent, unsmiling critic. My parents were members of a musical social committee through the synagogue they belonged to and occasionally meetings took place at our house. The piano came in handy for when they rehearsed songs for a show they were putting on. This was Mum's outlet for fun, but to me she always seemed to be showing off, flirting with the other husbands in front of Dad and trying to impress with a vivacious and carefree personality that went back in the wardrobe as soon as the evening was over. Dad was too busy chatting to notice the things I saw. In my black and white world, Dad was perfect, and Mum was to blame. For everything.

I couldn't have grasped this at the time but like it or not, children are witnesses to their parents' growing up. To a greater or lesser degree, and in our own way, we are all still finding out who we are and perhaps who we want to be, before our children take their first steps. As children we assume our parents are perfect and complete creations, but mums and dads will inevitably misbehave, test the boundaries, make mistakes, stamp their feet and shed tears before they become the men and women they need to be. And, so it was for both my parents in the end.

7

Judy Garland was singing in our kitchen because Mum had brought the *Dansette* record player in from the lounge so we could listen to her LPs while we made cakes. My baby brother, born a few months before, was having a nap but as I was older I wanted to do more adult things with Mum.

As Judy belted out *The Trolley Song,* Mum collected what she needed. A wooden spoon and the packet of *Viota Fairy Cake* mix was already on the table, next to the mixing bowl. As she checked the instructions on the packet, I read the list of songs printed on the record cover. I loved listening to this record because it was more exciting than any of the others we had. Looking back, this must have been my first encounter with a live performance recording. I thought this concept was unique to Judy Garland. The applause in Carnegie Hall at the end of each song, and sometimes at the beginning, when the audience recognised the song from the first notes, was so thrilling. At certain points Judy broke off from singing to talk. Mum knew the words to all her songs and the in-between bits where Judy spoke directly to the audience. When Judy said, 'thank you, I love you all', she sounded as if the applause was making her sad, and when Mum said it with her, she seemed to understand exactly how Judy was feeling.

I was waiting to hear *Stormy Weather,* my favourite song, and I wished it would come on because I had something important and secret to do upstairs in my bedroom while Mum was busy downstairs. It was a surprise for Mothers' Day. I'd had the idea a few weeks before when I was out running errands.

Since we had a baby I was allowed go to the local shops by myself to buy the small things that we needed. I had my best ideas when I went out on these walks, but I had to listen carefully to Mum's instructions, or she wouldn't trust me to go. She said that sometimes I was in a dream world.

"Concentrate on what I'm saying," she'd said. "You go into the butcher's and say you want half a pound of sliced ham, not too thin, and a quarter of corned beef. Then at the chemist next door, ask the lady to give you a small bottle of gripe water."

We were a Jewish family but not very strict about it because we ate pork. Mum sometimes lit candles on a Friday night but mostly she said we were heathens.

She put her yellow duster down on the kitchen table and took out her purse from a black handbag she'd left on the chair. "Here's the money. There will be change. Don't lose it and don't talk to strangers."

I knew the way, past the house on the corner with the roses growing near the front door and all the way down the straight long road to the roundabout. Look left, look right and look left again. All clear, and there was the butcher's shop, between the ironmonger and the greengrocer.

The shop smelt of bloody, raw meat, nothing like the delicious roasting smell in our house when the Sunday lunch was cooking. The man behind the counter had a pink face, almost the same shade as his sausages. I wondered what he'd say if he knew what I was thinking about his face. My good idea for what to buy for Mothers' Day came just as he turned away to slice the ham.

The next week, instead of catching the bus straight home from school I went to the department store across the road with Jacqueline. I'd been saving my birthday and pocket money to spend in the haberdashery department.

I chose a tablecloth with a rose design printed onto all four corners and leaf shapes stencilled in the centre. I only knew a few embroidery stitches, but this pattern was perfect because the roses could all be done in cross stitch and the leaves in satin stitch. I could do both of those. I selected embroidery silks in different shades of green and some reds for the roses. The package went in my school satchel and I found a hiding place for it at the back of the cupboard in my bedroom. This would be my surprise present to Mum on Mothers' Day. I giggled to myself when I pictured her face. She'll be all smiles when she sees how much hard work it took. Jacqueline promised not to tell her mum about my plan, so the secret was safe.

It had looked quite a manageable task in the shop but when I started on the work, I could see it might take longer than I thought, which is why I really needed to be upstairs working on it, rather than listening to Judy Garland.

Mum was humming the tune, but I could tell she was concentrating on putting the cake mixture into little pleated paper cases arranged on a tray. There were twelve of them altogether and she was struggling to drop equal amounts neatly into each one. I longed to have a go, but Mum only let me put the supplied red glacé cherries and green angelica decorations on top, the least messy part of the operation.

When the cakes went in the oven I slipped away unnoticed. It was only when I retrieved the sewing from its hiding place in my room that the enormity of the task sank in. Hundreds, maybe thousands of stiches were needed to complete the design. I decided to enlist help from a new friend.

A family with three children had moved in next door. Laura, the eldest was ten, a year older than me. We spread the tablecloth out on her bed, so we could work on different corners at the same time. Mothers' Day was the following weekend and a big push was needed. I wasn't too happy that my stitches looked a little careless in places but there was no time to be fussy.

With Laura's help, three out of the four roses were completed the day before Mothers' Day. It was a shame the fourth corner and the leaves in the centre remained untouched. I would have to finish it off after I gave it to Mum.

On Mothering Sunday I woke up to the delicious smell of bacon drifting upstairs. Mum loved crispy bacon. Dad must be getting it ready. He called up the stairs to say breakfast was on the table and I hurried down, holding my card and the folded tablecloth behind my back. I had butterflies in my stomach from excitement.

A bunch of fresh daffodils had been placed in the custardy yellow vase on the windowsill, next to a Mothers' Day card. My baby brother gurgled from his highchair and Mum was already sitting at the table when I presented my surprise like a stage magician.

"Abracadabra! Happy Mothers' Day. I've made something special for you," I said, making sure the corner with the tidiest stitching was the one she saw first.

"Oh, thank you," said Mum. She glanced at the tablecloth before putting it down on Dad's chair to open the card. Perhaps she didn't realise that the embroidery work was more than just that one corner on the top, so I started to explain.

"It's a tablecloth. For a table. With roses on. It took ages. I didn't have enough time to do the last one, but I can finish it."

She placed the card on the table by her plate and glanced in the direction of the gift. "Right. Yes, I can see. Very nice. Thank you for the card," she said.

Her voice didn't sound very enthusiastic.

"Those red roses are beautifully stitched," said Dad, but he wasn't looking closely because he was filling the teapot at the same time. and making sure Mum had everything she needed. As he took his place at the table he moved my present from his chair to the draining board, as if it was something you used to dry the dishes.

All the questions and delight I had imagined would be sparked by the sight of my handiwork were not forthcoming. The disappointment was crushing. I picked at my breakfast because it suddenly hurt to swallow. I vowed not to bother with bright ideas like this again. I'd get a much better response if I stuck to the safe but predictable, *Coty L'Aimant* gift set.

Thus, began my early education on how to give my mother the 'wrong' present. That Christmas, Dad's surprise gift got an even frostier response. The look she gave him when she opened the oblong blue and gold box spoke loud and clear. The box was so pretty it didn't need extra wrapping paper, but when she saw what was inside she behaved as if he'd deliberately purchased something he knew she wouldn't like. It didn't stop at a look either.

"Where did you get the idea that I would like this kind of watch?" she said, closing the box.

I looked at Dad and saw his eyes doing the fast blinking thing that happened when he was uncomfortable. I felt a familiar lump in my throat.

"I don't know. I thought it was quite dainty. I just hoped you'd like it," he said.

"It looks cheap to me. That must have appealed to you," she snapped.

"Never mind. We can take it back and you can change it. Choose one you'd prefer." She put the box down on the kitchen table, pushing it back towards him as if it was unworthy of further consideration.

"You should have asked me what I would like in the first place. You know I like to choose things myself," she said.

"You also said you'd like a surprise. Now I know better," he said taking the box, as if removing it from immediate view could somehow erase the offence.

"A surprise that I'd like, yes. Not that."

It made me angry that Mum could be so badly behaved and hurt Dad's feelings. I longed to let him know that I felt sorry for him, but I didn't know how to express it. When Mum went in the kitchen I stayed in the lounge with Dad, pretending to read a book I'd been given. My eyes were too full of tears to see the words properly. The adult world was so unfair. I was sure I'd be told off

56

and probably smacked if I didn't say thank you for a present, but Mum got away with everything.

Only much later did I begin to understand that, for Mum, presents were a visible demonstration of love. The giver's feelings or the idea that, 'it's the thought that counts', was beside the point. When gifts from close family did not accord with her taste or expectations there was no hiding this for the sake of politeness, because we, of all people should know what would please. If we got it wrong it could only be because we didn't give the matter sufficient thought and therefore, by implication, did not care enough about her. Naturally, she'd take umbrage if she suspected any gift she bestowed missed the mark, although I could never bring myself to say as much. It took many years, but we gradually evolved to gift vouchers to spend as you fancy in a favourite shop, or simply cash inside a card.

All through my childhood she remained unimpressed by cottage industry creativity, so home-made presents were a definite no-no. If it hadn't been purchased from a shop, it didn't count as a proper gift, it was just a token. It also had to be a personal, indulgent item, as opposed to something that was practical and useful.

My naive, hand-embroidered tablecloth fell short on several counts, given those exacting criteria. After handing it over I never saw it again.

In later years, unwanted shop-bought gifts were either overtly returned and exchanged or given away to someone else. Occasionally, after a decent interval, they might even be offered back to the giver. Mum didn't give house room to rejects for very long.

'You can make use of this. It's no good for me', was a frequent refrain.

I got wise to this in the end, so insisted on specific and unambiguous gift ideas. This proved a helpful gambit.

'Surprise me', was the instruction I dreaded. Such a loaded imperative with satisfaction not necessarily in proportion to the money spent. When the delivery of flowers for Mothers' Day became a convenient online service, I used it once. The next year I was told well in advance, 'not to waste all that money,' by having a bouquet delivered to the door. This was subtext for, 'If you're going to spend that much, then buy me something I would like.'

Months before she died she was still using the purse with the glittery clasp I'd given her, even though some of the paste gems had long fallen out. The relatively inexpensive amber and silver earrings, brought back from a trip to Poland, were still prized too, though these were not my greatest gift-giving triumph.

It was the time I booked a hotel and tickets to a West End musical for just the two of us that meant the most. Just as the house lights went down, she turned to me, her eyes bright with anticipation and delight. "This is fantastic. Such good seats."

"They are. Looks like a sell out too," I said as the overture began.

On cue, a piece of ill-conceived embroidery appeared before my eyes, fluttered in the air above the stage like an old rag, dissolving as the curtain rose.

8

I must have been about ten years old when Mum decided I was old enough to go on a train by myself and meet her in the West End. There was a lot to remember about the arrangements and Mum needed to be confident I understood what to do and where to go.

"Let's go over it again," she'd said, the day before. "When you get to the ticket office at the station, what do you say?"

"I say I want a single to Baker Street and give the man at the ticket office the money. Then I go through to the bit where the trains are and go left, down the stairs to the platform we always wait on."

"Right, and when you get to Baker Street station the train will stop there so you get off and where do you go?"

This felt like a big thing for both of us. I had an appointment at the orthodontist and Mum was trusting me to do most of the journey there on my own. She'd given me a ten-shilling note for the train fare and written a letter to my teacher, explaining why I needed to leave school early. I had to wait for Mum in the agreed spot outside the station, and then we'd cross the road together and walk up Baker Street, past Madame Tussauds on the other side, further on and across a few more streets, until we got to the sign that said Harley Street. Every front door was painted a glossy black but about halfway down on the left-hand side was an orthodontist's office, with my name written on one of the special grey folders in their filing cabinet. My orthodontist was American and very kind. I didn't like it when she tightened my braces, but I always tried not to make a fuss because I wanted her to be pleased with me.

This was a journey I'd done with Mum countless times before. Thinking about going by myself made me nervous, but when the day came, and I was standing on tiptoe, reciting my request at the ticket office, a little thrill of excitement went through me.

As the train pulled away I thought about all the things we liked doing together in the West End, just Mum and me. She enjoyed looking at the clothes and home wares in the smart department stores. If she bought something, it put her in a good mood.

No one had coined the term, 'retail therapy' back then but a picture of my mother browsing, with a *Marshall & Snelgrove, Debenham & Freebody*, or *Selfridges* branded carrier bag in hand, springs to mind whenever I hear it used today.

On those trips, depending on the time of day, we either had lunch at the Orchard Room in *Selfridges*, where the waitresses wore dresses with a vivid green leaf design, or we had tea and a pastry at *John Lewis*.

If Dad was with us we usually ate in a restaurant. He used to work in the kitchens of some of the big London hotels and knew a lot of people behind the scenes. When he sent a message to the kitchen, the head chef often came to our table and said hello to us at the end of the service. Mum particularly enjoyed these moments because it looked like we were more important than the other customers. My favourite restaurant was downstairs at

Lyons Corner House, where all the chefs wore tall white hats and wheeled trolleys of roasted meats to each table. There was something very theatrical about the style of service at this place that fascinated me. When the chef lifted the lid of the silver tureen on his trolley, it slid slowly back, like the visor of a knight's helmet, to reveal an enormous joint. While the chef was carving the meat into neat slices, waiters and waitresses would appear at our elbows with silver dishes of vegetables, divided into sections to separate the different kinds. Holding a spoon and fork in one hand, they could pick up the vegetables and place them in an exact spot on the plate. Nothing was ever dropped on the perfectly white tablecloth. It was like a magic show.

''Carrots, sir? Potatoes, madam? How many?'' they would ask, and they called me 'Miss', like a proper customer, not a child.

As the train to Baker Street de-dummed along I wondered what we'd do after the appointment. Mum might let me go to the record department at *Selfridges* to listen to the Beatles' latest song. Maybe we could look in the haberdashery department, where all the reels of coloured cottons, embroidery silks and knitting wools were displayed. Some of the classes at my school were knitting coloured squares in plain stitch, for a blanket to send to children in poor countries. Perhaps we could choose the wool for me to do it, but there was no more time to think – the train had come to a halt and the one other lady in the carriage was already on her feet, waiting for the doors to open. I'd been so busy daydreaming I hadn't noticed the journey at all. From the window I searched for the big signs with the name of the station, just to make sure I was getting off at the right stop. Yes, this was Baker

Street, so I needed to think carefully and remember what Mum had said.

It was all a bit confusing because there were two exits, one in front of me and another to the right, past the newspaper stand. I stopped there for a moment, watching people buying copies from a large pile. The picture on the front page was of a boy wearing glasses. It was one I'd seen before on the television news. He was called Keith and although he was smiling and happy in the picture, everyone was worried about him which kind of made it worse. He was supposed to be going to his grandma's house near Manchester, but he'd disappeared on the way there and no one could find him.

The station clock jolted me back to reality. It said nearly twelve, which was the time I should be meeting Mum and I was still standing inside the station.

I went straight on, exactly like she said and reached the spot where she told me to wait. There were so many people walking past it was hard to concentrate, but I kept looking in the direction I thought she would be coming from. She was having her hair done first and I knew where the hairdresser was in relation to the station. It might have been easier all round if I'd gone straight there but that would have meant crossing a main road.

She seemed to be taking a long time and I was starting to feel a bit hot, so I took off my school blazer and folded it over my arm. She must have told me a dozen times to stay in the agreed spot. I kept telling myself that she would appear at any minute, but I had no idea how much time was passing as I stood there, looking and waiting. After a while I started to feel uneasy. Maybe I should walk down the street to the other exit, just in case she was waiting there.

It took a few minutes for me to pluck up the courage to move. This was what she had specifically told me not to do, and when I did finally get there my worst fears were realised. No Mum. There was only one place left to try in my mind. I would have to cross the road and go to the hairdresser. I was so sure this was the obvious solution.

I waited at the kerb and followed the other people across the road. I found the entrance to a little arcade and looked for the chemist's shop right at the end. It had a certain type of hairbrush in the window that we also had at home. I passed a couple more shops before I saw a familiar image of a lady with black wavy hair on the inside of a glass front door. As I went in the foggy odour of hair lacquer and nail varnish made me feel a bit sick. I wanted to speak but the receptionist was on the phone, studying the appointment book. She was wearing bright blue eyeshadow. It looked lovely. I almost forgot what I wanted to say when she finally put the phone down and looked up at me.

I was struggling to be understood above the roar of the hairdryers and it was difficult to hear her reply because of the din. "Oh love, she left ages ago," I heard. She called to one of the stylists in the salon beyond, "Pauline, Mrs M's daughter is here. Do you know what time she left? Over an hour ago, wasn't it?"

I didn't want her to say another word. My heart was beating so fast she must have been able to hear it. I shouldn't be here. I'd moved off the spot where I'd been told to wait. I ought to get back. Quickly.

I retraced my steps as fast as I could but by now I felt tired and upset. I was nearly there when a hand came from nowhere and a hard slap landed on my bare arm, again and again it cracked down. "There you are!"

My eyes closed as the first blow made contact but when I opened them I saw, to my horror, two police cars parked outside Baker Street station. Mum was shouting something, an apology and an explanation to the officer coming towards us with a notebook in his hand, before she turned her fury on me again. "I told you not to leave that spot! I've been worried sick. Wandering off is the one thing you were told NOT to do."

"But, Mum, you weren't ..."

"Don't you dare argue with me after the trouble you've caused."

I couldn't understand why she was so angry. She found me when she thought I was lost so why wasn't she thanking God I was safe? I've replayed this moment again and again in the years since and I still wonder if she would have reacted differently if I'd burst into tears and flung my arms around her in relief.

We disappointed each other that day, but I wasn't equipped to make sense of it, so I just sat in miserable silence as she fumed all the way home and for the next two days. The orthodontist must have wondered why we didn't arrive that afternoon and I hoped she wouldn't find out that it was all my fault.

I decided not to watch television that evening. If I'd caused my mother so much worry that she called the police, it was sure to be mentioned on the six o'clock news and all my friends would know about it. I went to bed early, but I couldn't get to sleep. I kept thinking about Keith, the boy in the newspaper and how his mum cried when he'd gone missing.

******

This was roughly how it went with us in the years that followed. Unexplained, unexplored small disappointments on both sides, with larger hurts, adding to the wall between us. At first, we could still see each other over that wall but brick by brick, over the years it grew taller and wider until we had to search to find the remaining gaps in the structure we'd constructed. We both hit our heads against that brick wall from time to time.

Some twenty years after the incident at Baker Street Station, Mum and Dad had divorced and both had different partners. I was living in Adelaide, South Australia. My husband's job took us there and we were trying to start a family, but a pregnancy was proving elusive. I was having hospital investigations and because I was so far from home and my husband was frequently away, I felt frightened and lonely. I wanted to confide in my mum. She'd lost babies herself. This was the sort of stuff mothers and daughters shared, wasn't it? Up to this point she'd never been an overtly supportive kind of mother but this was a different situation, I told myself. Intimate, personal.

When we left for Australia, I hoped she and my stepfather, David would come for a holiday, but after two years there were still no plans on the horizon. I never expected Dad to come. It was very clear that his new wife held the purse strings and a trip to Australia, to see his daughter, would not have been countenanced. It was Mum I needed, or perhaps I was subconsciously testing her. In any event, I thought if I explained, she'd feel important and that might swing it. She'd surely *want* to come. It was my clumsy attempt to forge a connection between us. I poured it all out on thin blue airmail paper, so convinced that I'd get a sympathetic reply by return. My overactive imagination was setting me up for disappointment. As soon as it was posted I imagined her showing David the contents of the letter. They'd be surprised and concerned. We had no idea and of course we must go, they'd say.

Back in the real world my letter failed to hit the emotional target I'd aimed for and they didn't come. I received a reply that glossed over my worries but no real explanation as to why they wouldn't be visiting Australia. I filled in the gaps myself. It was obviously inconvenient timing. A change of partners meant there was a new home to establish and no spare money for a trip like that. My distress was simply not a good enough reason to find the money at the time.

When we returned to the UK, for good, a year later, two things happened. I fell pregnant immediately and Mum and David booked a holiday in Australia.

9

Summer started early the year I turned twelve. On those long, light evenings, my parents sometimes chatted with our next-door neighbours over the garden fence. From my bedroom window I could see Dad, bending to trim the edges of our lawn with shears, whilst on our neighbour's side, Mr Brent, Laura's dad, inspected his tomato plants. He had a nifty way of checking for ripening fruit with one hand as the other reached for the roll up he always had in the breast pocket of his shirt.

A skinny cigarette dangled, unlit, until he straightened to locate his matches deep in a trouser pocket. Ignition, by a deft, one-handed movement, along the box edge, a protective hand cupping the flickering light, head tilted to one side as the chin led the flame to its target. Deep breath in, eyes closed, mouth closed, the out breath visible in twin nasal columns. Actions he repeated at least forty times every day. That's what I heard Dad tell Mum afterwards. Apparently, when he was younger, Uncle Bernard used to smoke forty a day too but gave up years ago.

Mr Brent was more of a career smoker though, with tell-tale facial creases etched into leathery skin from every deep drag he'd ever taken. The ease with which he handled cigarettes and matches, plus his black hair reminded me of Humphrey Bogart.

When I shared this thought with Mum she said I had a vivid imagination.

The clip, clip of Dad's shears continued until Mr Brent's crackly voice floated across the fence. "Evening, Les. Lovely spell of weather for a change, eh?"

Dad looked up when he heard his name and waved. He looked grateful for the interruption. He scrambled to his feet to continue the conversation at the fence, mopping his face with a white cotton handkerchief and wiping his glasses as he went.

On evenings like this our mums might be in the garden too. If the men were talking, then sometimes the women exchanged superficial pleasantries. Mum wasn't the type to encourage female acquaintances to come over, uninvited for a cup of tea and a chat. It would upset her routine and she said she found that kind of thing very dull.

Laura's mum had striking green eyes, high cheekbones and olive skin. People told her that she looked a little like Sophia Loren. She made the mistake of sharing this with my mum. Later, it was relayed back to us in tones of high-pitched scorn. "Sophia Loren? Do me a favour! She's not unattractive but she's pushing it a bit there. She'd *like* to look like Sophia Loren!"

'Not unattractive' was about the closest Mum could get to giving another woman a genuine compliment.

Laura was already a teenager, but I still had a year to go. We were best friends and I liked the atmosphere in her house. She was allowed to put posters and pictures of the actors from *The Man from U.N.C.L.E* all over her bedroom walls for one thing. When I asked if I could do this too, the answer was no because it would ruin the wallpaper. It seemed extremely unfair that it was fine for Laura to ruin her wallpaper but ours had to be protected.

I was invited to go with the Brent family on a caravan holiday. It was the summer that *God Only Knows* by the Beach Boys was a hit. We couldn't get enough of that song. We made friends with two boys from another family who were also staying on the site. We were all still children, sitting on a farm gate stealing kisses and exchanging addresses, promising forever and ever with an intensity that hurt. We were playing heightened, exaggerated versions of ourselves, over-reacting to the lyrics of a pop song, that we thought the adults couldn't possibly understand.

Laura had her first period while we were away, and her mum took me to one side to explain very kindly why Laura might not want to go in the sea for a few days. I felt like I'd been given special and confidential knowledge about the mysterious, womanly territory I had yet to enter.

Soon after we returned, Laura's dad went to work and never came home. I heard Mum and Dad whispering something about a massive heart attack. There was an empty, aching sadness in her house after that. I thought about how Mr Brent used to light his cigarettes in that special way of his and that I wouldn't see him do that ever again. The silent, jagged edges of life and death were piercing my skin and secondary school was about to add a few scars.

Mum thought the private school was making me too prim and proper. The state system would toughen me up a bit, she said. Around this time my parents had a few financial problems and school fees were expensive. Dad had been persuaded to invest in a grocery and delicatessen shop but after a promising start the business had failed and there were debts to pay. Dad always looked worn out when he came home and for a while my parents spent a lot of evenings, looking at the accounts in a bid to find out why there were no profits. Mum suspected that the business problems were something to do with her father. He was helping Dad run the shop, but I'd only met him once and didn't really think of him as a grandpa. Not like Poppa.

Everything hinged on the eleven plus exam. If I passed I could go to Laura's grammar school. I passed everything except Maths, so the grammar school turned me down. My future was decided and a few weeks later I entered the hostile, foreign country of the secondary modern.

I might as well have had a sign round my neck inviting the bullies to go right ahead. Everything about me, from my babyish pink coat to the glasses I needed to wear in class, attracted them. It didn't help that I was keen to do well. For reasons known only to Dad, he'd purchased a small brown suitcase for me to carry my books to school. Even if they overlooked the rest, the suitcase was all the excuse the bullies needed. I was soon cornered after school by some older girls who opened my suitcase, spilling the contents onto the pavement and threatening more of the same or worse the next day.

I'd only been bullied once before. At primary school a spiteful little girl with long plaits called Rosemary used to punch and bite me. Mum had a sharp word with her mother, which didn't help as she refused to believe that her little darling could possibly do such dreadful things. Rosemary left the school for a more prestigious establishment the following year, much to everyone's relief. I decided my parents needed to know what was happening to me at my new school, especially as these girls were a lot more threatening. Things improved after Mum made one of her signature telephone complaints to the head mistress, but I also learned how to be a lot less conspicuous. I didn't want to hurt Dad's feelings, so I quietly retired the suitcase. Straw baskets were the school bag of choice for girls, and as survival in this new environment depended on my ability to fit in, I rapidly acquired my own.

The culture of this school was so different from everything I knew about the world to date. Half a dozen pupils, belonging to a few notorious, local families, were scattered amongst the year groups. They were the grubby, unkempt ones that were often sent out of class for disruptive behaviour. They never did their homework, were always in trouble for arriving late, losing their books, and failing to wear the correct uniform. This was a new tribe of human to me and my kind was clearly unknown to them.

A few weeks in and I was asked to look after a girl called Jane who had moved to the area from Scotland with her mother. Her parents had spilt up and her mum had met a new man. Jane didn't seem too impressed, but she had no choice in the matter.

We were all struggling to make sense of the confusing changes happening to our bodies and our minds. By the third term two of our bright, smart classmates had mutated into snarling, greasy-haired, truants after their parents split up. Both girls had left comfortable family homes to share sleazy bedsits with their respective mothers. A girl in my class quietly developed anorexia before anybody really understood what that meant, and another was sent home with a headache one day, never to return. The following morning, we learned that the quiet, mousy girl who

71

made very little impression on us when she was alive, had died from a brain haemorrhage in her sleep.

We didn't dare speak about our feelings or our fears and no one encouraged us to do so. Instead we avoided each other's eyes, in case one of us exposed our vulnerabilities by making the unspeakable a topic of conversation. The dead girl and her family played on my mind for years. Even now, I still wonder if someone remembers and misses her.

Soon after this tragedy we were all sitting on the hall floor listening to the usual boring assembly announcements. Chairs for the teachers were placed at the side so they could keep an eye on the students and shush them if they started talking. Mrs Westfield, the head of Domestic Science was seated at the end of our row. I worshipped Mrs Westfield and everything about her lessons. She was married to the Head of PE at the boys' school, next door, and they arrived together by car in the mornings. They were not a particularly good-looking couple, but they had produced three white-blond, beautiful children that we sometimes glimpsed from afar. Mrs Westfield was quietly spoken, very calm and kind, but authoritative. To me she was the epitome of motherly perfection and the fount of all knowledge on home-making and happy families.

The assembly ended, and we got to our feet. A girl called Caroline, in the row in front of us, was having difficulty standing up and did so in a somewhat awkward way. Caroline's attendance had been irregular of late and she'd put on weight since I last saw her in school. As we turned to file out of the hall I saw Mrs Westfield's jaw drop open. I followed her gaze, by which time Caroline had got to her feet and was standing side on, like a ship in full sail. It was obvious to everyone looking that Caroline's recent weight gain was an eight-month pregnancy. Mrs Westfield would doubtless have identified an underage pregnancy at an earlier stage, had Caroline been in her Domestic Science group. As she signalled her obvious concern to another member of staff, we turned to each other and the whispered accusations travelled down the line.

"Look at her! It's obvious!"

"You kept teasing her about putting on weight."

"It wasn't just me and how was I to know she'd got herself into trouble?"

"What's she going to do now?"

The very worst thing that could befall us – aside from death – had happened to a girl we knew. It was shocking and so very strange.

Outside school I was still best friends with Laura. She had her mum's green eyes only rounder and bigger. Her mouth was shaped exactly like Twiggy's so when she was all made up she had the perfect look. Slim, with the long legs I knew I would never have, Laura was ready to launch herself into the unknown world of boyfriends. I still felt like a child next to her, but I was learning fast. She showed me how to fold over the waistband of my school skirt to make it fashionably short and was introducing me to other things, like smoking. A connection between smoking and the early death of Laura's dad, didn't enter our heads. Our GP smoked a pipe in his surgery. Perhaps Laura felt a kinship with her dad when she lit up and that's why she persisted with it.

On a Saturday, out of parental view, she produced from her coat pocket, a pack of ten *Players No 6* cigarettes, with the distinctive turquoise and green stripe on the box. We took one each and ran to the telephone box on the corner to light them out of the wind, before catching the bus into town. The record shop, next to the Wimpy Bar was where all the teenagers went.

Classes were not mixed at my school, even though the boys were on the same site and were only separated from the girls by a white line in the playground at break times. The staff room overlooked the line and any movement by either sex in the wrong direction earned a detention. Romance was therefore conducted from a tantalising distance and furthered after school or at weekends.

Some of the best looking boys from school were frequently found at the record shop on a Saturday, where they soon fell under Laura's spell. She was like a magnet to boys. In the next few weeks my popularity with the opposite sex seemed to take off and the attention I attracted impressed my classmates for a while. I made the most of it because I knew it was an illusion. The boys were only seeking me out after school to find out if my good-looking friend would be making a repeat appearance in town at the weekend.

Laura and I borrowed each other's clothes. Or more accurately, Laura did the borrowing and I did the lending. I kept it secret because Mum thought wearing other people's clothes was disgusting. It was a whole lot simpler to just put the requested item under my coat and slip out before she noticed. She would only interfere if she saw me handing over items like the brand new, black handbag I'd bought with my birthday money. Mostly it was down to me to supply a favoured bag or a piece of knitwear when Laura was going on a date. Everything looked better on her anyway, although I was beginning to resent the fact that my items were not always returned.

The next time I saw my black bag on Laura's arm all the newness and shine had gone from the leather. I didn't have the guts to say anything and the friendship eventually fizzled out when she left home at sixteen to get married. The relationship didn't last and when I ran into her a few years later, the sparkle in her green eyes had gone, disillusion and drudgery putting paid to her good looks. Nicotine stained her fingers and front teeth, just like her father's.

Socially, I was like a chameleon. My school friends were the group I belonged to during the week, but my parents had steered me towards a Jewish youth club, so my weekends were often spent with different friends, in synagogue halls, dancing to records and trying to impress the boys.

I'd been introduced to drama and elocution at my primary school. A flamboyant teacher had entered a few of us into competitive festivals and I'd won a silver medal for reciting one of Hilaire Belloc's *Cautionary Tales* at one event. Birthdays often meant a trip to a West End theatre with my parents to see shows like Lionel Bart's *Oliver! The Sound of Music* or a Christmas pantomime, starring a big name like Cliff Richard. Later on, we saw the controversial musical *Hair*, though I don't remember that being my choice. I was certainly uncomfortable with the nudity in parental company.

My secondary school offered very little for a budding thespian, so I had to search elsewhere for what I was missing and found a youth group led by Bunty, a former stage actress. Bunty chain-smoked and coughed her way through every rehearsal. It was a miracle she didn't suddenly expire like Laura's dad, because she was a lot older than him. Under her direction and hacking cough we put on plays in a community hall and it was fun to be part of a team of actors. As one of the youngest I only played minor roles, but I learned a lot from the more experienced players and Bunty was very encouraging. She always invited the local paper to write a review and it was exciting to see whose names were printed, a sure indication of the performances that had most impressed the reporter. I even got a brief mention on one occasion. I hung on all five words that covered my appearance in the play and kept the cutting for years.

It suited me that these activities and groups stayed separate and distinct from each other. I was very confused about who I was and who I wanted to be. Consequently, I didn't feel completely myself with anyone. It was the Jewish side of things that was problematic.

Anti-Semitic remarks were commonplace at my school, and I decided it was safer to ignore them rather than call attention to myself. The prejudice went in both directions. I wasn't too confident that my Jewish friends, some of whom were much more religious than my family, would understand why I had so many non-Jewish friends. Maybe I wasn't 'Jewish enough' for my Jewish friends? My Dad didn't take time off work for the religious holidays and I still went to school as normal. And we didn't give two hoots about the dietary laws. I didn't discuss any of this with my parents. The thought of bringing any of this into our house was shameful, as if by acknowledging my worries and talking about them, I would be found at fault. I was fearful of being judged and found wanting by anyone. It was all so complicated, but I clung to the belief that all my little worlds could continue turning without interruption, if everyone stayed in their separate zones.

Perhaps my personal identity crisis at the age of fifteen, went some way to explain why I alone found Trixie Best an appealing personality.

Trixie arrived like a force of nature, a new girl in our fourth form class. Loud, bold and socially clumsy, she shared my interest in the performing arts. If I was more comfortable with who I was, I might have introduced her to my extra-curricular drama group, but of course I didn't. With little or no outlet for her talent at school she became the star of her own daily drama. Beanpole tall and ruddy-cheeked, her tiny blue eyes were always alert for opportunities to disturb the prevailing atmosphere. If we were all concentrating in class she jangled everyone's nerves by dropping a heavy textbook from a great height, falling noisily off her chair, or calling out something banal in her unusually refined accent. Her extensive repertoire also included, inundating teachers with inappropriately timed questions, shouting out the answer instead of putting up her hand, making late and noisy entrances to lessons, laughing at other people's mistakes, and generally behaving like an immature brat. Cheers or boos, Trixie didn't mind. As long as there was an audience, she was happy.

She had difficulty pronouncing the letter 'r', so she referred to herself as 'Twixie', and me as 'Wooth', holding fast to her vocal tics, despite the constant teasing it brought her. The bullies would poke fun at her, to her face and behind her back but I sensed they, like me, secretly admired the way she shrugged them off just by stubbornly staying herself. She towered over most of them, which certainly gave her some physical advantages, on the occasions she chose to lash out with a well-aimed punch. Mostly she remained oblivious to their taunts. The bullies were wasting their time and eventually moved on to easier prey. She didn't care if her behaviour risked alienating her peers and many of our teachers. I was slavishly doing all I could to be the same as everyone else, while 'Twixie' remained supremely comfortable in her uniquely annoying skin.

The only time our class did any drama was with a student teacher, and we both threw ourselves into it with alarming enthusiasm. What started as a rivalry gradually turned into mutual respect, albeit delivered with adolescent hostility.

I'd developed a hormonal ability to cry at will and managed to pull this one out of the bag in a role play exercise focussing on characters under pressure. Trixie cornered me in the cloakroom at lunchtime, curiosity bursting out of every pore.

"Wooth, howdya just *do* that, anyway?" she said, elbowing me in the ribs, her usual way of initiating conversation.

"Hey! Do you have to do that?" I said, doubling over to protect myself from further assault. "What are you on about?" I knew what she was asking but pretended otherwise, just to make her beg.

"You know – cwhy! Just like that. Go on, show me how you do it. Go on."

"I can't just *show* you. It comes from inside. I think about something that upsets me and it just comes over me. Miss Green thought there was something really wrong," I added hoping that this titbit would further impress. Trixie's little blue eyes widened.

I left her, still staring at me in wonderment as I picked up my bag and walked away.

Soon after this exchange Trixie let slip that her parents were very old. I told her that mine were too – my dad was *forty*, a whole ten years older than my mum.

"Huh! My pawents are much older than that," she scoffed.

"Are you like your mum or your dad?"

"Don't know."

I persisted. "You *must* know."

"No! How can I know? My pawents, the ones I live with, are not my *weal* pawents, you idiot! I don't even wemember my weal pawents. Don't you understand? They didn't want me, so I was adopted when I was a baby," she said. This was voiced as a statement of fact, seemingly without a trace of self-pity.

I didn't respond directly to Trixie's revelation. Not knowing who your parents are must be so weird, but finding out they didn't want you, might *make* you weird. The bell for afternoon lessons interrupted my conjecture, muting any further conversation we might have had on this topic.

10

I lived in fear of Mum's temper, not so much the moment she lost it with me but the way her anger hung in the air for hours, and sometimes for days after. It wasn't just the behaviour that displeased, it was the perpetrator too. As if she, and she alone had been singled out for torment by a sullen and awkward adolescent, devoid of any redeeming features.

Admittedly, even my normally placid Dad could be roused to anger when I subjected my grandmother to a miserable, monosyllabic conversation on the phone but at least I knew where I was with Dad. He had a cross word about something specific and then it was over. What set Mum off was subtle and unpredictable. Sometimes I wondered if envy could be fuelling her anger and frustration. Perhaps I was an irritating reminder of what she missed out on by marrying Dad when she was only nineteen.

It had been drilled into me to ring home if I was going to be later than anticipated but it wasn't always that easy or convenient in the days before mobile phones. Finding a phone box that worked and reversing the charges through the operator was the routine. It only took one failure to cancel out the countless times I'd adhered to the rules.

"Midnight, she comes in, without a word! You're a thoughtless girl, only thinking of you, you, you! We were sick with worry until we heard the key in the door. I'm putting an end to your gallivanting and don't think you're too old for a smack either."

The punishment was brutal. No going out on Saturday night. This called for drastic action because I *had* to go to the dance that everyone else was going to.

Clutching my shoes on the night, I crept downstairs in the dark whilst my parents were watching television. I opened the front door as quietly as I could and just as I was about to make a run for it in stockinged feet I heard Mum say to Dad, "Ach, don't run after her. Let her go – I remember my Aunt not letting me out. I swore I'd never be like that."

It's a refrain I often heard, that she didn't want to be like her Aunt Becky, but despite what she said it happened anyway. It was as if Aunt Becky's voice came out of her mouth without her permission.

I didn't set out to provoke her, but she was hard to please and refused to see anything from my point of view, even when the obvious was staring her in the face.

The day she dragged me to the outerwear department of *Selfridges* I was soon fighting for my teenage life over a coat she picked out for me. She took a step back from the full-length mirror, a look of triumph on her face, as she inspected my appearance from the back. I was bristling with a mixture of embarrassment and malevolent adolescent discontent at the sight of myself in a funnel neck coat, in a luminous shade of orange. We were in full view of the shop floor staff and any other innocent customers that happened to stray into our war zone.

Orange was a colour she might have chosen for herself, but it was toxic to a self-conscious teenager, trying to cultivate an image of mystery and allure. The tone and volume of Mum's voice carried to another customer, innocently browsing through our battlefield. She retreated to a safer distance once Mum started on me.

"Take that look off your face and stand up properly. The neckline is beautiful. It's so 'with it'. You're just being awkward as usual. It's a beautiful coat for the winter."

I knew there'd be no room for an alternative viewpoint. Her verdict was final and incontrovertible, but I gave it my best shot. "I hate it. I look like a tangerine." I tried twisting my neck in an exaggerated attempt to free myself from the fabric that insisted on brushing my jawline. I held my arms at an unnatural angle, away from my body, in a pitiful attempt to distance myself from the object of hate that covered them.

"I don't know what you're talking about," she countered. "It's a bright and cheerful colour for a change. Put your arms down and keep still. The neckline is supposed to be like that. One day my girl, you'll have an ungrateful daughter. Then you'll know how it feels and you'll be sorry. Walk up and down over there and let me see how it hangs on you."

I managed a few paces, a deliberate flat-footed, round-shouldered stomp that I knew would annoy her even further. She practically pulled the coat off me and headed towards the cash desk to conclude the sorry business.

Several months later, the tangerine coat and a lime green trouser suit remained unworn and unloved at the back of the wardrobe. Unless.

"I'll wear them if you let me dye them black at the dry cleaners. Black is going to be the 'in' thing this winter."

My argument fell on deaf ears, as I knew it would.

"You must have another think coming. Don't you dare! Black, she wants! Black, schmack! What funeral are you going to?"

In a rare act of defiance, I saved up all my pocket money and did it anyway. There was something so irreversible about black dye that the only weapon left in her arsenal was ridicule. I wore all the dyed items until, in her words, 'they dropped off me' and my so-called 'black winter' became the stuff of family legend.

Battles with Mum, particularly over clothing, started way before my teenage years, though. From the age of six or seven she made me wear white cotton gloves when we went out, which I loathed. It was like sensory deprivation having my fingers and hands covered by material and I removed them at every opportunity, much to her annoyance.

Eventually, she gave up on the gloves but on one of our West End jaunts she took me to a very expensive shoe shop where the assistant brought out a pair of fancy black patent children's shoes. Photographs of me wearing these shoes in Italy suggested they were purchased for this family holiday. The shop didn't go in for the careful measurement of children's feet and those wretched shoes pinched my toes from the start.

After what was probably a very short interval, I tried to convince Mum that my feet had grown, and I needed different shoes but to no avail. Looks were everything and because she said they were 'beautiful Continental shoes' they had to be worn, until she decreed that they had done sufficient service. Oh, the irony! In years to come, I would willingly subject my feet to worse cruelty in platform heels for the sake of fashion, but at least that was my choice.

At a time when my very existence seemed to infuriate Mum, I did something right by bringing my self-assured new school friend, Linda to her attention. For one thing Linda, unlike me, enjoyed wearing smart, brightly coloured clothes.

"Such a straightforward, sensible girl!"

Linda happened to be Jewish which was another reason Mum warmed to her, but Linda tended to make a positive impression on most adults. That was why she'd been made Head Prefect. I was just an ordinary prefect, a drone to her Queen Bee. They were scraping the barrel with me because, unlike Linda, I wasn't altogether comfortable wielding authority, but I liked the privileges of being a prefect, such that they were. These mainly involved extra access to the tuck shop. Linda enjoyed the power and walked the appropriate walk in school with ease. Outside school, with a confident, possibly overconfident personality, she was a man eater.

Linda owned the ground with every step of her dainty, turned-out feet. She was short and slightly stocky, but ballet classes gave her a ramrod straight back and the illusion of greater height. Blessed with absolute self-belief and a very thick skin, nothing really phased or embarrassed her. This was handy as I was inclined to doubt, deliberate, decide and then regret most decisions. On the downside, she could make me cringe at the directness of her approach, especially when the opposite sex was involved. She picked her targets and homed in with ruthless accuracy, whereas I tended to admire from afar which generally had no impact whatsoever. Linda was all about results.

One Saturday afternoon we met up with a couple of boys we were desperate to impress. They seemed to be waiting for our suggestions on where to go rather than offering any ideas themselves. This was Linda's dream scenario, a chance to organise everyone, just like my mother. Before I really knew what was happening, she decided we would all go back to my house. I was very uneasy about this turn of events but tried my best to look unconcerned in front of the male company. My parents were out and I wasn't sure when they would return. If the boys didn't stay too long it should be OK. The idea that they might return whilst everyone was there was unbearable. Dad was bound to do something embarrassing and Mum was sure to say something to humiliate me in front of everyone. I tried not to let any of this anxiety show in my face but it must have been obvious.

The long walk from the station to my house didn't impress the boys very much. Finally, I put the key in the door, and we piled into the kitchen. The room was unnaturally full of tall male strangers that didn't fit into our space. Then the trouble began.

"I'm starving after that walk. Got anything to eat?" said one of boys.

"Oh, er, there might be something in the fridge, I don't know. I'll have a look. There's some cheese here," I said, my hand alighting on the first item that came to hand.

The other boy wasn't about to wait for me to find out what meagre scraps the fridge might yield. He was already off his chair and reaching upwards to the cupboards. "Whatcha got in here?" he said.

I watched in disbelief as he reached in, moving the sacred tins to read the labels until one took his fancy. I wanted to scream, 'What the hell do you think you're doing? You can't do that here!'

The tiny whimper that escaped from my mouth went unnoticed.

He had a nerve helping himself, but I realised that any negative intervention risked spoiling the carefully crafted atmosphere of casual entertaining I was aiming to convey. I just didn't have the confidence to object, and maybe he knew that too. All the while Linda remained oblivious to my agony. The cupboard taboos didn't apply in her house.

"This'll do. Tomato soup," said the boy after a good rummage.

I jumped as he slammed the cupboard door shut with an uncaring bang and handed me the tin.

"Right. I'll just warm it up then," I said.

Linda was already laying the table like a good wife, so I poured the soup into a pan and lit the gas, as if serving tinned soup to impromptu visitors was something I did all the time. Meanwhile the other boy raided the bread bin and located the butter. It was hard to keep track of what was being moved and rearranged. The kitchen was rapidly turning into a crime scene. As the interlopers ate, I looked at the ticking kitchen clock, wondering how much time it would take to remove all evidence of this prohibited meal.

After the food was eaten, to my relief, the boys got bored with the lack of action at my house and left with Linda in search of adventure without me.

I thought I'd got away with it. Everything had been washed, dried and put back in its place but less than a minute after my parents returned, I was summoned to the kitchen. My mother was pointing to the violated cupboard. "Perhaps you'd like to explain what's been going on here?"

I followed her direction upwards and saw a perfectly formed black thumb print on the white surface, left by the intruder.

It was a lot simpler to lie than to go anywhere near the truth. If she knew I'd brought people back to our house that were capable of such depravity, my life would have been a misery for days to come. And the shine would have come right off Linda too.

I concocted a scenario on the spot. Coming home I felt cold and shivery and hot soup always helps, doesn't it? I embellished the tale with enough detail to be plausible, mentioning I might have been a bit cack-handed in my haste to locate the right tin, but I really wasn't feeling very well.

She peered at me doubtfully, putting a hand to my forehead to check for a raised temperature which I knew she wouldn't find.

"But I feel much better now," I said, in a bid to head off any further investigation.

"You're like a bull in a china shop. Is it too much to ask that you wash your hands first? There are black finger marks all over this cupboard that need scrubbing off."

Exaggeration was one of Mum's favourite ploys, generally used to induce maximum repentance from the guilty party. Mum didn't believe in the idea of children doing household chores. I heard this regularly and it was all the excuse I needed to never lift a finger or offer to help. What would be the point? I was never going to do anything to her satisfaction, and she didn't have the inclination to tutor me in her idea of perfection.

"If you want something doing properly, do it yourself," was her motto. It was far better to get out from under her feet and let her get on with it.

She couldn't rest until all evidence of interference was purged from the cupboard's interior so the emptying, soaping, wiping and replacing of tins to their rightful positions filled the next two hours. The atmosphere in the kitchen was thick with resentment, mixed with just a hint of martyrdom as Dad and I retreated to the watch television together in the lounge.

Smoking is something I really didn't want my parents to know about. What if someone else told them I smoked? That had the potential to bring down all sorts of maternal retribution.

Which was why I pulled out all the stops on the day Mrs Pike caught a group of us smoking in the toilets. Mrs Pike was the Deputy Head and also my English teacher. I was one of her star pupils, so perhaps the punishment wouldn't be too severe. We all filed into Mrs Pike's office to learn our fate. A couple of us were prefects so we were ceremoniously stripped of our badges. I could live with that. It was when she mentioned a letter being sent home to our parents that the survival instinct really kicked in. The sudden rush of adrenaline must have aided my creativity. As my peers turned to go, I heard myself asking if I could speak to Mrs Pike privately.

An audience was granted and I gave the performance of my life, turning on the tears to good effect. "I've let myself down and set a bad example to others by such a dreadful and deceitful act," I heard myself saying. "My parents will be heartbroken and just now, when they have so many other things to worry about, I've added to their misery and I just, can't begin to guess what impact this will have on them," I sobbed. I was breathless by this point but realised a pause was needed before a dramatic conclusion. "A letter like that could be the last straw. For all of us."

Mrs Pike listened to this without interruption. I spent a good deal of my free time amusing my friends with an unflattering imitation of her vocal delivery, and the way she skipped sideways between the rows of desks in our classroom to give out paper or books. I strove with every fibre of my being to put this vision out of my mind for fear it might show in my face, thus ruining the impact of my speech. I waited for her response, heart thumping in my chest.

"Very well. There won't be a letter to your parents on this occasion. If things at home continue to worry you, do please come and see me. You're on course for some excellent results and I wouldn't like to see that compromised."

I could only believe that my passion for her subject, coupled with the contrition my peers did not think of showing, must have swayed her. It was a handy way to learn that my drama skills were transferable to the real world.

As soon as we turned sixteen a few of us signed up with agencies offering temporary office work in the West End during the school holidays. It was well paid, plus we could learn useful stuff, like working a switchboard. Switchboards were not all the same but I learned to bluff my way through the unfamiliar systems. This usually meant suffering a morning of acute embarrassment, cutting off every call, in a bid to find out how to operate the equipment correctly. If the office was near Oxford Circus, I looked at the shops at lunch time or ate in a café. Part of the fun was negotiating the route on the Tube and going to different places. It was a great way to earn money in the holidays, but I wanted to do something more exciting when I left school. Number one on the list was journalism. English had always been my best subject at school and working for a newspaper or a magazine was something I was sure I'd be good at, if someone gave me a chance.

Most of my friends had Saturday jobs at hairdressing salons or shops but I worked in a Jewish deli on a Sunday morning. It was a short train ride away and I had to be there at 8.30am. This was a challenge if my Saturday night had been particularly exciting but whatever happened, I was always on time and never called in sick.

I overheard Mum telling someone else on the phone that I wasn't lazy, like some teenagers, and always got myself out of bed on time to go to work early on a Sunday. It sounded like she might be just a little bit proud of me. Perhaps I had some positive attributes after all, but they were never made known to me directly.

'Ach, what a nightmare you were as a teenager, such a drama queen. Exasperating! Always, aggravation and worry, is what I had with you,' was the message I received, despite what she told other people.

11

North London, 1970s

Dad's cousin was a Fleet Street editor, so a call was made to ask for advice on how I might enter the field of journalism. It wasn't encouraging. If I went to his newspaper office, I'd only be allowed to make the tea. Apparently, it was a very competitive world with very few opportunities for girls. So much for contacts in high places. University was mentioned but that was pie in the sky. Students from secondary modern schools were not regarded as university material.

An interview at the Careers Centre was even more disappointing. The middle aged, bottle blonde with scarlet nails and lips was specially trained to bring hopeless dreamers to heel. Advice was predicated on the idea that you mostly told kids from secondary modern schools what they *couldn't* do. Aspiration hadn't been invented. It was all about keeping you in your place.

"A journalist? Oh, I think you had better lower your sights a bit, dear. I don't think so," she said.

Her pronouncement was final. As she didn't offer any further guidance there was nothing more to say, but she did me a favour in crushing my ambition out of hand, without knowing the first thing about me. I left her office with a determination to show her and all the other useless advisors like her that she was so very,

very wrong. Even if it took the next twenty-five years, I'd show her all right.

Meanwhile I considered the other subjects I was interested in at school, like domestic science. The curriculum consisted of practical cookery and the theory of food and nutrition. We spent a lot of our time designing menus for a category of people called 'invalids' or small children whose young bones and teeth required a calcium-rich input three times a day. I was pretty good on the theory but envied my friend Jane's practical ability. Her scones always rose higher than mine, her Genoese sponge was lighter, her biscuits shaped and baked with uniform precision, whereas mine always turned out disappointingly misshapen. I had triumphs one week and failures the next. And there was another thing about Jane that I envied. Her metabolism. She remained spectacularly thin, despite her enormous appetite for high calorie food. Being her friend inevitably meant adopting some of her eating habits. Her mum worked for a cake and biscuit manufacturer, so she had access to a constant supply of treats at home, which she was more than happy to share. This was supplemented by daily trips to the baker's and sweet shops for more supplies on our way home from school. On this regime, and to the amusement of others, I was piling on the pounds while she looked like she ought to be lying down with a drip in her arm.

Ironically, considering my weight issues, I played with the idea of being a dietician, but this proved problematic as it required studying physics and chemistry. Only the girls at the grammar school took these subjects. Annoyingly, the boys next door at my school studied physics and chemistry, but to be fair, they were denied needlework and domestic science. A half-hearted discussion by the teaching staff on whether I could be allowed to join the boys' classes for the mysterious sciences ended with a predictable no.

What else could I do? Drama was an obsession, but I'd deliberately not mentioned this to the dragon at the Careers Centre. I didn't need her or anyone else to tell me that acting wasn't a viable option for someone like me. Attending a prestigious stage school in London was the best way to be cast in shows, adverts and films, but I was a realist. Stage school was expensive and the few kids I knew that went there were from rich families.

Dad had been studying for a teaching qualification and he'd taken a job as a senior lecturer in the Hospitality and Catering department at Ealing Technical College. In the absence of any better ideas I was enrolled there on a two-year course in Hotel Management. Dad wouldn't be teaching me, but many of his colleagues would. Before I put a foot over the college threshold I felt disastrously self-conscious and very unsure whether being the daughter of a member of staff would be a blessing or a curse.

If most of my peers at Ealing College had dreams of becoming hotel managers, they were dreams I didn't share. Three weeks into the course and I was arriving late to class, staring out of the window, when I should be taking notes, and stubbornly ignoring every opportunity for education that the college put my way. Every day seemed longer and more miserable than the last, but I didn't know what to do about it. I felt sure that the lecturers were only indulging my less than satisfactory attitude because my father was a colleague.

During that endless first term I prayed someone would notice that my poor performance was a symptom of unhappiness and thus put me out of my misery without me having to say anything to Dad myself. There was something about Dad that made you want to protect him from hearing bad news.

I reasoned the lecturers could only turn a blind eye for so long. The day of reckoning must surely come. Better that way than having to admit to Dad myself that my commitment to a career in hotel management was non-existent, and that certain failure beckoned.

My mother had no such inhibitions about delivering uncomfortable news to anyone, quite the reverse, but we were not confidantes. From her point of view, I was out of the house, gainfully and purposefully occupied.

Out of the blue, one evening I got a call from Trixie Best. She rang to find out what I was doing because she was at college, studying drama. I steeled myself for a difficult conversation, hoping I could inject some brightness in my tone to disguise the misery.

Dad was out and Mum was busying herself in the kitchen. She'd recently had the kitchen door removed, in a further attempt to inflict open plan, contemporary living on us all so my side of the telephone conversation was being broadcast from the hall, loud and clear.

"Oh wow! Drama! What sort of things do you do? Reading plays, did you say? Voice and movement? It sounds amazing. What are the other students like? And the teachers? How long is the course?" I was so full of questions, but it was hard to listen to the answers without being overwhelmed with envy at Trixie's life.

Trixie being Trixie, didn't seem too interested in hearing what I was doing, and I wasn't too keen to talk about it, so I let her continue with her favourite topic. Herself.

As she prattled on about the various personalities at her college, I felt isolated and hopeless. When she talked about her ambitions to be a drama teacher, I told her I needed to go.

Everything I'd hoped for and wanted for myself was happening to other people. I was just a bystander, catching a glimpse of their light from the bottom of a deep, dark pit. I remained silent about how trapped I felt. I was enough of a disappointment to myself. I didn't need to rub it in by disappointing everyone else as well.

Much later that night, from the top of the stairs, I heard my parents talking, or rather Mum was talking and Dad listening. That's generally how it went in our house.

"Leslie, I'm telling you, Ealing College is not right for her. You were the one that pushed her into it. I said it was a mistake at the time. I'm always proved right in the end."

"She hasn't said anything to me about it."

"How can she, when you moved heaven and earth to get her in? I heard her talking to her school friend on the phone about drama. It's obvious that's what she really wants to do. You'll just have to talk to the principal and explain that she's leaving, won't you?"

Mum didn't waste time or sympathy by talking to me but what she said to Dad in her assertive, no nonsense way that night meant I didn't have to explain any of it. Perhaps she understood me better than I cared to admit and was prepared to stick her neck out for me when it really mattered.

95

The autumn term was well under way, so it was too late to change direction and start another course straightaway. I needed to wait and apply for the next academic year. Meanwhile, I could earn some money doing full-time temp work. I had a purpose and a plan. Everything around me changed from dull grey to vivid colour overnight. I was energised, enthused, and raring to find a drama course.

Before the internet we only had the library and the telephone directories to find out basic information, but soon after posting an application to Kingsway College of Further Education, I was invited to attend an informal interview with the drama course tutor, JJ.

Tall, with piercing blue eyes and the charisma of a film star, JJ was the first openly gay man I'd encountered and the most brilliant and inspirational teacher I've ever known. As I waited to be called, groups of students huddled round the door of his office, eager for a sighting and a word with their guru before he interviewed the next hopeful on the list.

Later that day I saw him in action with a second-year class that clearly adored and respected him. He was kind, but he was no pushover. Those laughing blue eyes flashed venom at latecomers, the ill-disciplined and the lazy but in the next moment he would say something amusing to bring the wayward back into the fold without the least bit of resentment on either side.

To my joy, a letter arrived a few days after the interview indicating that my application had been successful. The new academic year was still several months away, but I'd just landed a long-term temping job at the West London offices of the London

Electricity Board, so my excitement at what was to come had to
be put on hold for a little while longer.

At huge cost, the LEB employed dozens of temporary staff,
specifically to handle calls from customers who were querying the
enormity of their electricity bills. The irony of this was not lost on
us at the time. The London Electricity Board was finally
privatised in 1990, presumably when someone noticed that the
organisation was haemorrhaging money by relying on expensive
and incompetent temporary staff.

This was nothing like a modern call centre. There were no
computers, so it was, by today's standards, a primitive form of
customer service, run by confused amateurs with limited
understanding. Every day we did whatever we could to keep
awkward queries at bay, by consulting pages of handwritten notes
recording each customer's electricity consumption. It was like
trying to make sense of coded messages in a foreign language.

Most of the female temps were Australian, in their early
twenties or younger. They weren't on a gap year as we understand
it now. These girls were working their way round Europe with no
intention of ever returning to the Sydney or Melbourne suburbs
if they could help it. London was their Holy Grail and the best
place to get a temporary job. They all lived in shared flats around
Earls Court, which they sometimes invited me back to. I was
embarrassed at how childish my home life seemed in comparison
to theirs and I kept much of the detail to myself. Some of the
accommodation was grim, but to me the hardship was all part of
the perceived glamour that went with freedom from parental
control. I was going back at night to good food on the table, a

warm bathroom and *Dralon* settees. I couldn't have been more ungrateful.

The British temps were a mixed bunch. Some of the guys had been drifting in and out of jobs in their hometowns and were now giving London a go. A few of the girls had followed their boyfriends to the big city and were playing at being couples. One or two, like me, were planning to resume our education. Fran, the oldest, was in her mid-twenties, wore black kohl liner around her eyes and an armful of silver bangles that tinkled prettily when she picked up the phone. She'd been to university, drove a noisy VW Beetle and only started working for the LEB because she didn't know what else she wanted to do. That was two years before, and she was still there.

Other temps came and went, some only sticking it out for a week but a hardcore group of us remained. The longer you stayed, the more you learned about how to deal with complaining customers, which made it interesting.

We worked in an airless room at one of four tables equipped with several ancient black phones. Most people smoked, so a heavy fog hung over the space on most days. I could take or leave smoking by this point. Like my mother, I treated smoking more as a fashion statement than an addiction. The walls of the room were lined with shelves, holding row upon row of black, leather bound folders, each containing hundreds of pages of records for every home with an electricity supply in the area of London we covered. At the top of each page was the name of the bill payer, followed by the address and then in chronological order, logged by hand, their meter readings, either the real figures or estimates based on previous usage. A baffling amount of additional detail, relating to tariffs, price per unit of electricity and payment schemes was also included. Supposedly, this gave us all the information we needed to assure customers that their bill was indeed correct or, if the evidence suggested otherwise, what the next steps might be.

Only one person in the room could genuinely decipher this information and talk to customers about their bills with authority. This was Dolly, the only full-time staff member. Dolly had given the LEB the best thirty years of her life. With Edna Everage specs and tightly permed hair, as grey as the ash dangling on the end of her cigarette, Dolly was like a mother hen to all the temps. She could always be relied on to take over when a telephone conversation with an irate customer looked like it might be going in a direction that took us well out of our competence zone. I was hopeless with figures, and I was by no means the only one with shortcomings in this area, so Dolly was often in demand. It was probably when she was on a well-earned holiday that I developed my own strategy for dealing with complicated queries over billing. Agreeing with the customer usually took the heat out of most exchanges.

"That does sound rather high for the last quarter, doesn't it, Mr Patterson? I think we should send a meter reader round for another reading, so we can check that the meter is functioning as it should," was a line that worked a treat. In reality, faulty meters were practically unknown.

Whilst I set in motion the human expertise required to inspect said meter, I also had the authority to put a stop on the account, so poor Mr Patterson didn't have to worry about being cut off for non-payment in the interim. Of course, it was all a pointless waste of time, manpower and money and several weeks later, when the meter reader's report was received, Mr Patterson had to cough up. Giving him the benefit of the doubt bought him a little more time though, and more importantly, got him off my back.

The most memorable moment I had at the LEB was when I came across the electricity records relating to a M. Jagger Esq of Cheyne Walk, whilst searching for those belonging to a lesser mortal. Studying that page of impenetrable digits, which were never queried to my knowledge, was practically like touching Mick Jagger's electricity meter. A truly thrilling prospect. Temptation was too great, and I sent a meter reader round there, just because I could. I constructed an elaborate but very pleasurable daydream around this which involved Mick being interrupted mid-song by the doorbell. After a long pause, he would eventually open the door, a fleeting look of questioning wonderment in his eyes at the stranger standing there in a peaked cap.

"Come to read your electricity meter, sir."

Dressed in a flowered shirt and with his trademark ruffled hair, 'Sir' would lead our man to the imagined cupboard under the stairs. Detached and professional, his hands trembling slightly, I fancied him completing the task to the unmistakeable guitar riff from *Jumpin' Jack Flash*. Naturally, Keith and the rest of the band would be amusing themselves in the basement, until their esteemed vocalist returned.

The workplace was my refuge because the atmosphere at home was often tense, especially if Mum was in one of her moods. Meals would either be eaten in silence or superficial conversation between my parents masked an undercurrent of hostility from Mum. One slip up, and all hell would break loose. One evening I was supposed to have turned the oven on and laid the table in readiness for everyone's return and I failed to do so. I was probably thinking about something more important to me at the time, but this was interpreted as deliberate malice on my part and the accusations quickly escalated out of control. Dad tried to be the peacemaker and from my listening post at the top of the stairs I heard him pleading my case in the kitchen. "It's not the end of the world, is it, Sylvia? She just feels that you're always against her. That she can't do anything right. Why don't you just say sorry?"

There was a pause, a sniff, and a dismissive grunt. "I don't ask her to do much, Leslie. Selfish and thoughtless she is, and you always take her side against me. I'm telling you now. Either she goes, or I go."

"Now you're being ridiculous."

I didn't really expect Dad to choose between us. I knew this was the sort of wounding and illogical argument she fell back on when pride stood in the way of a climb down, but her comment felt spiteful and chilling all the same. It was true I was still Daddy's girl. It was Dad that made our house a home. Most of the time Mum made it an uncomfortable place to be and I knew Dad felt it too. The tyranny of the vacuum cleaner if he dared to have forty winks in the lounge on a Sunday afternoon. Everywhere the chemical smell of the cleaning fluids and hair spray she insisted on using daily, the snarky retort, if he dared make any comment on it and the frostiness that lingered in the air afterwards.

When Mum's favourite furniture polish started being advertised on TV, Dad and I groaned in unison at the sight of a product that already dominated our lives. No wonder we roared with laughter when, despite the advertising and Mum's devotion, the company ceased trading.

Perhaps she'd sensed those little moments of togetherness between us and had come to see me as a rival for Dad's affections. I didn't want a rival or an enemy, nor a sister or a friend. Just a mum. I sat on my bed, confused and unhappy, with a heart-shaped stone lodged deep in my chest. I'd felt that stone before and it hurt, but now I welcomed it as a part of me I recognised.

12

After weeks of rehearsals, under JJ's expert direction, we were ready for opening night. He'd taken on a diverse group of teenagers and made disciplined actors of us all. I'd always found it easy to learn lines, but all my previous experience with Bunty's drama group in obscure one-act plays seemed trivial and amateur compared to this. For a start, JJ had selected a full-length drama by a playwright people had heard of. The subject matter was hard-hitting too, pitting the establishment against a group of travellers. I played an unsympathetic social worker and my character was in the opening scene. I didn't have the talent or interest for musical theatre. Gritty realism was much more my bag, and I couldn't wait to perform the play in front of an audience.

Show week comprised several public performances for the college community, our friends and families. After the dress rehearsal, a whisper went around the group, as we were about to go home.

"JJ's boyfriend has turned up."

"No?"

"Where?"

"Over there, standing by the door, looking miserable."

A dozen pairs of teenage eyes swung towards a slight, restless individual in an oversized leather jacket, with dark, greasy hair falling untidily across his face. He looked no older than most of us, and when he shook his head to dislodge an overhanging lock, the gesture revealed clusters of teenage acne mapping both cheeks and a jawline scarred by pock marks. I'd always imagined JJ's partner would be his equal in looks and age, and the reality unsettled me. A few of us discussed this on the train home but we soon moved on. Of more immediate concern was which night our parents were coming to the show and whether they'd like the performance.

I told Mum and Dad to arrive early on the first night to be sure of a good seat. One of the stage crew let me know he thought they were seated in the front row from the description I gave him. After the show, maybe they'd meet JJ. All the students wanted their parents to meet JJ.

I waited in the wings, hyper-alert, to the order of events we'd rehearsed.

"When the audience are in their seats, the house lights go down and you'll hear the opening of *Runaround Sue*. After the second verse, the music fades, then lights up, and Ruthie, you're on!" JJ had told me.

I was trembling with excitement and when Dion's intro about two-timing Sue came through the speakers, it was my cue to take a few calming breaths.

The "hep, hep" of the backing singers silenced all the pre-show chatter and then the lights went up and I was in that space, speaking the character's lines and nothing else existed. My world was only this moment with these make-believe people. I couldn't see the audience through the glare of the stage lights but the applause at the end told us all that we'd done ourselves and JJ proud.

I emerged after the show, hair adrift and smudges of stage make-up still visible, breathless from the post-show excitement backstage. There were so many people milling about in the hall, I couldn't focus on anyone at first. Then I saw them. Dad was shaking hands with JJ. My two heroes, and as I snuck in by Dad's side, I heard JJ talking about me. "One hundred per cent reliable and always so helpful and enthusiastic. A real pleasure to have a student like her in my class."

He turned to me and with genuine warmth in his eyes, squeezed my hand. "Super performance tonight love, well done."

Dad beamed as these words of praise hovered in the air around our little group. "You were brilliant," said Dad, putting his arm around my shoulder, "we could hear every word, you spoke so clearly." For a moment, we were all rapt, suspended in a bubble of mutual admiration.

"Helpful? Reliable? Are you quite sure you're talking about *my* daughter?" said Mum, addressing JJ.

She had to say something and maybe she thought that by puncturing the atmosphere with a barbed rejoinder she was being witty. Perhaps, in a fit of pique that the attention was not directed at her, she felt the need to impress on her own behalf. I was crushed, not so much by what she said but JJ's uncomfortable smile and the way he looked over Dad's shoulder, inviting the next in line to catch his eye, thereby offering a swift escape.

I was in the kitchen, a day or so later, looking through my college notes as Mum laid the table. I'd been expecting this conversation.

"Well, so what did the great JJ think of your mother?" She referred to herself as 'your mother', perhaps to distance herself from this other, needy woman she knew.

"What do you mean?"

"He's a charming man. He must have been surprised to find that you've got such a young mother," she added a hand gently patting the back of her hair, as if JJ was in the kitchen with us, assessing her appearance as she spoke. Is this all she cared about? What *my* teacher thought of *her*?

"He didn't say anything," I said without looking up. "He meets parents all the time. He's got other, far more important things to think about." My words were deliberately chosen to wound. The tight angry feeling that I used to get in the pit of my stomach when I was younger had come back again.

She made a funny little noise in her throat that signalled she had reason to believe that JJ was indeed very complimentary, it's just that I was refusing to tell her.

******

It must have been at least twenty years after this conversation that I sat, alone in the staff room of a school in rural Cambridgeshire. I had a free period and was leafing through the pages of a respected national newspaper. A familiar name in the obituary section caught my eye. A coincidence, surely? No, the details of an outstanding career in theatre and education indicated that this was my JJ. I read the tribute, but in my head,

I was adding my own paragraph, explaining how he supported my ambition for further study, guided me towards teacher training and encouraged my application to a prestigious London drama school. My application was one of a hundred and sixty received that year. Only thirty places were available. I didn't think I had a chance but JJ's faith in me was rewarded. His loyalty and support continued. He came to see my degree show, writing a letter to me afterwards full of thoughtful observations and kindness.

I swallowed hard, but too late, the tears were falling. The bell for morning break rang and any minute my colleagues would come bursting in, chattering about their morning and last night's television. They couldn't see me like this. I dried my eyes and quickly scanned the obituary again, but no details of the cause of death were given. He hadn't even reached retirement age, so perhaps it was a life-limiting condition, but the usual form of words was missing. There was no hint of a 'brave struggle' or 'after a short illness' in the text. Maybe it was sudden and unexpected. A car accident or a heart attack.

I cut out the column from the paper and put it in a box of keepsakes at home. I found and re-read the letter he wrote me, the looped, precise script once more in my hand. The author, no longer in this world.

Eventually, I found out how he died. At a college reunion, one of his former colleagues trembling with rage, explained what the obituary couldn't say. JJ died from an AIDS related illness following a cruel and fatal betrayal by his long-term partner, the restless youth with the leather jacket and bad skin.

******

At about the same time that JJ suggested I could train to be a drama teacher my parents had a peculiar conversation. Mum's announcement sounded so outrageous I struggled to remain silent from my listening spot on the top stair.

"A friend of mine would like me to go away with her for the weekend and I've said yes."

"Oh? What friend is this?"

"No one you know. From the hairdresser. I see her every week. We got talking. Just a break for the weekend. She hasn't been well. She thought it would do her good but then she thought it wouldn't be much fun, going away on her own. So, she's invited me along."

"Where does she have in mind?"

"Rome, actually."

"Rome! Are you out of your mind?" I heard Dad say.

"Just for the weekend. It's all booked and above board. I'm going next weekend."

Silence. No further information offered. No inconvenient questions asked.

It was screamingly obvious to me that the unnamed female friend didn't exist at all and that this was a cock and bull story to cover an affair. Mum simply didn't have the sort of intimate female friends that this scenario implied. I was silently urging Dad to ask to ask more questions or to object and demand to know the truth, but my unheard pleas from the top of the stairs were missing the point. He didn't want to know the truth. I'd never felt more miserable and helpless than that moment, when my father let my mother's lies go completely unchallenged. I didn't know how this was going to end but it already felt like a downward spiral to the bottom. I retreated from direct contact with my mother as much as I could. Conversation between us was monosyllabic but Dad seemed to carry on as usual. I couldn't read what was going on in his mind, but I suspect he was trying to ignore the red flashing signals ahead.

Just before this, a college friend had introduced me to a charismatic, blue-eyed Dutchman. He was only a few years younger than my father and I was besotted with him. It was a timely distraction and meant I could avoid dwelling on the situation at home.

The romance was helped along when he spent time in London, visiting highly intelligent, wealthy professionals who were willing to open their homes to him and his much younger girlfriend. Apparently, he 'helped' people. From my observations he seemed to be a cross between a shaman and relationship therapist.

He travelled from the Netherlands to the UK for this mysterious work every few weeks, which added an element of intensity to the relationship that was novel and exciting. When he was in London we saw each other every night. It all felt very grown up and sophisticated and just a little bit outrageous. I was, after all, enjoying an intimate relationship with a man old enough to be my father. As I saw it I was having a much more interesting love life than most girls of my age. It didn't last for long, but it happened at the right time.

Occasionally, when college holidays coincided with his travel plans, I went with him. We had a few weekends away, staying in hotels in the south of Holland and in much less interesting, East Grinstead, a place of immense significance connected with his line of work.

I was glad of these opportunities to be out and away from home and my parents were too absorbed with their own issues to put many obstacles in my way. When Dad answered the phone on one occasion and remarked that the man asking for me sounded surprisingly 'old' I managed to gloss over it.

Despite his transient presence, I felt safe and secure in this man's company, even after it transpired that my Dutchman was somebody senior in the Church of Scientology. It didn't dawn on me until much later that our East Grinstead rendezvous was chosen so he could attend a meeting at the home of the religion's founder, Ron L Hubbard.

I was often privy to some strange conversations among the converts, but no one asked me about my beliefs or tried to persuade me to join them. Perhaps they assumed I was already one of them. I listened, when over a meal in an expensive restaurant he explained the fundamentals of the religion to me. A series of weird diagrams, drawn onto paper napkins accompanied a lengthy exposition. Apart from the bit about reincarnation, which I found quite appealing anyway, it all sounded quite literally, double Dutch to me. It was a struggle to stay engaged, but I nodded and made encouraging noises every so often to disguise my bafflement.

Prior to this relationship, I had a boyfriend of my own age. He was an overbearing, controlling force, crude and immature which made for a volatile combination. It had all started to get a bit intense, so we called it a day by mutual agreement. I explained this to my mature, level-headed Dutchman and I was intrigued when he suggested that my emotional health needed to be tested. He produced a peculiar device that looked like two tin cans wired up to some sort of meter. I held the cans, one in each hand, waiting for the needle on the meter to settle to give a reading. It was off the scale. Just as well we didn't get around to discussing my relationship with my mother.

Things came to a head at home soon after Mum returned from the weekend in Rome. I arrived back late from college one evening to find my parents sitting unhappily in the kitchen's fluorescent glare, with something they needed to tell me. I sat down next to Dad. He was slumped in his chair with an expression somewhere between shock and grief and Mum just looked grim. She'd confessed the truth about her trip and a further bombshell had been dropped. My parents were splitting up and she was leaving. The other party had already left his wife. They were part of the same social circle as my parents and we knew the family. My younger brother would remain at home for a while but would live with Mum and someone called 'David' as soon as they were settled.

My face was a mask. My father looked as if he had been punched. I couldn't look at my mother.

My attempt at self-protection was hastily misinterpreted as level-headed acceptance. The focus of attention and care was rightfully on my much younger brother and making a difficult adjustment as easy as possible for him. He was only ten and I was nineteen. I was supposedly the one best able to understand that relationships sometimes faltered, or so my mother told other people, as word got around. But of course, I wasn't. And I didn't. I was too frightened to express my real feelings because I had no way of controlling them, so I accepted everything without awkward questions or messy dissent. Inside I was howling with the hurt and anger of it all, but no one wanted to hear that noise, least of all, Dad. And it was Dad I cared about.

I didn't say it out loud. I didn't even whisper it, but I knew in my heart that I would always choose Dad over her. I wish I'd found the courage to shout it, so they both understood how I felt. Mum knew Dad and I were on the same team. It showed in the way I sat down beside him, not her and looked into his eyes, not hers.

So I functioned on autopilot, burying the hatred in my heart for his sake. Seeing my unhappiness would only remind him of his own powerlessness. His way of dealing with it was to adopt his usual, 'never mind, let's get on with it' approach. That's how it seemed in the first few months anyway. The feelings I suppressed at the time found their way out eventually.

As it turned out, my brother, a much more adaptable and easy-going personality appeared to take the new reality in his stride or certainly made a better fist of it than I did.

This was all happening in the wrong order to the wrong people. It was the children that were supposed to grow up and leave, not the parents.

I couldn't say how long after her announcement she went but it wasn't the next day. I don't even remember her packing her things or the first few days without her. I just came home one day and sensed that she'd been and gone, taking my brother with her. It hadn't turned out to be an idle threat after all. Now it was just me and Dad.

An autumn day was ending, and I was the only one at home. I'd dared to imagine a time when I had this kind of freedom, but now I had it, I didn't know what to do with it. The tick of the kitchen clock filled the silence in every room of the house like a drumbeat.

Downstairs in the lounge, as if in a dream, I stood in the dark at the bay window. I pushed a net curtain aside and with my face close to the glass, looked out into the empty road. The light from the streetlamps picked out the slight movement of drizzle in the evening air. A sudden shift in consciousness, a heightened awareness and I turned back to look at the room that she'd created. I could overturn the table, pour tea over the settees, draw on the walls, grind muddy shoes into the carpet. My outrageous fantasy gave me no pleasure. It was too extreme.

This was my house now. My rules. Moving quickly, I switched on all the lights and went to each side of the bay window in turn, lifting the hooks to release the tiebacks from their moorings so they hung down, lifeless. Starting on the left side I gently coaxed the floor-length orange material from its perfectly aligned position, easing it along the curved rail until it reached the centre point of the bay. Then the same on the right side until both curtains were completely drawn, and the rest of the world was excluded from view for the very first time.

The era of 'just for show' was over.

PART TWO

1

Sylvia
East London, 1935

Her mother had named her Sylvia but a few still insisted on calling her Rose. This is her story, pieced together from what she managed to find out, though the people she relied on for information either couldn't recall the details or refused to talk about them. She wanted to know so much more as she got older but by then there was no one left that could tell her.

As a small child she slept in the same room as her adoptive parents, Becky and Jack. Some nights, when Jack was out and Becky was fussing round her, she longed to be left in bed. Curled up under the covers, a ringlet of dark hair around her little finger, she liked to sing one of the cheeky music hall ditties that Jack had taught her. *My Old Man* was a favourite and she copied the way he sang it until her little voice dillied and dallied its way to the land of Nod, as he liked to call it.

Some nights she might still be awake when she heard him come in. He always looked in to check on her first and if she could manage it, she'd keep her eyes tightly shut, because she wanted him to believe she'd been no trouble and was fast asleep as she should be. He would bend down and gently stroke her hair or caress her cheek. In his touch she felt the great love there was between them, but the game would be up if he saw an eyelid flicker and the smile she was trying to hide.

"Ain't you in the land of Nod yet?" he would say with a chuckle.

When she was a little older and if it was still light, Becky allowed her to wait up for Jack to come back from work. She would take up her position at the parlour window and as soon as he was in sight she would run to meet him, and he would gather her up in his strong arms and all would be well for the two short hours until it was bedtime. Inevitably, details of her conduct that day would be relayed. Becky would complain that Sylvia hadn't eaten or hadn't opened her bowels and what was she to do with her, but Jack only laughed and gave his little girl a loving cuddle.

In fact, Becky and Jack were Sylvia's great aunt and uncle but this was a minor detail to the neighbourhood gossips, or *yuchnas*, as Becky called them. It was well known that Sylvia was an adopted child and so her progress was of much greater interest to the community than the regular offspring. Being an over-anxious type of woman, Becky feared the judgement that would inevitably rain down on her should anything adverse happen to her most precious possession.

From a baby in her pram and until she went to school, Sylvia went with Becky to the market on a Friday morning to buy food for *Shabbos* dinner. Whatever her faults, Becky was a skilled cook and an efficient housekeeper.

On one such Friday morning, from a bedroom window, Dora, one of two spinster sisters in the house across the street, watched their tall, red-headed neighbour close the front door behind her. Shopping bag in one hand and gripping the hand of her small charge in the other, Becky headed towards the market.

Dora called to her sister in the next room, "Come quick, Yetta, if you want to see Becky's little girl. I'm opening the window."

Yetta ran headlong into the room, pushed her sister aside and hung out of the window as far as she dared, before the unsuspecting subjects disappeared from view.

"Tch, tch, look 'ow Becky dresses her! Beautiful, no *schmutters*, neither. Always spotless too. I don't know 'ow she does it," said Yetta, shaking her head in wonderment.

"Out of bad comes good," said Dora. "Jack's always been a reliable provider. Come away now, Yetta and shut the window, the damp air's no good for my chest."

Excitement over, the two sisters returned to their chores, regretting that *mensches* like Jack were in such short supply.

Jack had been a tailor in a sweatshop before the Great War. He'd met and married Becky just before enlisting with the Royal Flying Corps in 1917. Unlike so many of his generation, he survived and returned home. He'd served as a cook to the airmen and on discharge became a dock labourer. Every day he'd leave home at four in the morning to stand in line for work. Somehow he always managed to get picked when others hoping for a day's pay were turned away.

Becky and Jack were not especially religious but their Jewish identity was strong, and the Friday night rituals were always observed. Candles were lit and a special meal prepared. It was only the strictly religious or *frummers* that had to cook their food before sunset, as any work activity after sundown on the Sabbath was forbidden. Some of the bakeries in the area offered a helpful service to the devout. On a Friday, pots of uncooked cholent stew could be taken for overnight simmering in the bread ovens and collected after the *shul* service on Saturday.

The market on a Friday was always noisy and crowded and as Becky moved slowly forward, Sylvia came upon a forest of moving arms, legs and shopping bags. She lowered her head, so people's coats wouldn't flap in her face and saw live chickens in a cage, pecking at their feet, their raucous cries mingling with the sing-song inflexions of the traders. In a blink of a little girl's eye a practised hand appeared to grab an unsuspecting fowl by the neck. Up and away it went for kosher slaughter and feather plucking. A little further on, through the cacophony of squawking, shouting, and hawking, Becky and Sylvia came to a halt at the fish stall.

It was a damp, miserable day, but Sylvia wore a thick coat, buttoned up to the neck, whatever the weather. Becky believed that layers of clothes protected against illness. Even on warmer days, when she played outside with her cousins, Sylvia still wasn't allowed to remove her coat.

The woman at the fish stall smiled down at the little girl, offering her a small pickled cucumber from a nearby tray. Sylvia stood on tiptoe to take it whilst the giver gently pinched her cheek. The woman's hands on her face smelt of herring.

"Gawd, Becky, such a little beauty she is, and those big eyes, a real little doll," said the fish seller, and in a loud whisper, as she reached into the herring barrel. "What would have become of 'er without you and Jack, doesn't bear thinking about eh?"

"Yer, right there," said Becky, with a nod to confirm the purchase. "Er father couldn't be relied on that's fer sure, and even less so now 'e's got a new family to look after, but 'e was always trouble." Becky shook her head at the fish seller, who made a few sympathetic noises as she wrapped the goods.

Sylvia stared at her shoes and took a little bite from the cucumber. She'd heard those things about her father before and she didn't like them. No one ever mentioned her mother. Perhaps Becky told them they weren't allowed to.

Becky had all the proper documents that said Sylvia belonged to her and Jack. She'd made sure it was an official adoption and not just an informal family arrangement. Even so, the situation still troubled her, and despite what she told others, in her heart, she worried that Sylvia's father might snatch her back one day, or worse still, when the child was old enough to decide for herself, she might choose him over her and Jack. All the more reason, she thought, to head off that possibility by ensuring Sylvia knew that they had come to her rescue because her father hadn't wanted her, that he was no good and but for them she would have been placed in an orphanage, like poor little Oliver Twist.

"You're a very lucky little girl, Sylvia and you'll always be grateful to your Aunt Becky, won't you?" said the fish seller, winking in Becky's direction as she handed her the parcel. Grateful was a word Sylvia heard a lot. She knew it meant that she must try to please Becky.

Jack thought differently. He believed it was wrong to sow seeds of confusion in the little girl's mind and make her think badly of her own father, but Becky stubbornly trod her own path, whatever he said.

On the rare days when there was no work, Jack liked to take Sylvia down to the docks to watch the ships unload their cargoes of tobacco and sugar. If they stopped to talk to the men he knew, he always referred to Sylvia as his daughter. She looked up at him, bright and happy when he said 'my daughter' because it sounded warm and loving.

At home in Copley Street, an extended family of protective adults all had a hand in Sylvia's upbringing. Becky's brother, Bob and his family lived in a downstairs room of their house and Clara and Golda, Becky's two unmarried sisters lived upstairs. More relatives lived in similar arrangements close by, in rented houses where the lavatory was outside and a tin bath hung on the wall in the scullery. Trivial disagreements and fall outs between Becky and her siblings were common but these were always put aside if one of them was ill or out of work. As Jack's employment was the most regular, Becky, the self-appointed matriarch of the clan, supported her siblings and their families with food and money when they ran short. Such was her generosity that even if they disagreed with her approach to childcare, they kept their mouths shut. Whether they liked it or not, they were beholden to Becky and keeping her sweet was in their interests. Uncle Bob forgot himself one Friday night, though.

The family were waiting for Clara and Golda to return from work. Clara was a 'clicker' in a boot factory and Golda was a shop assistant. Once through the door, the women abandoned their hats and coats and rushed to lay the table before Becky had a chance to reprimand them for being late. Bob, his wife Fanny and their two daughters, Mille and Bessie were called to the table. When everyone was assembled, Jack lifted Sylvia up to watch Becky light the candles and recite the blessing. Everyone said 'Good Shabbos' to each other and soon after, delicious smells wafted through to the small room where they ate, signalling that food was on the way.

While Becky fried the fish, she barked instructions to her sisters. They were already darting back and forth because they knew what needed to be done but that didn't stop Becky from telling them anyway. Cut the *challah* bread, take the jar of *haimisha*, pickled cucumbers to the table and don't forget Jack's favourite chopped herring.

When the food was on the table the conversation centred on the health and welfare of other members of the family living nearby and Clara's fears that the factory manager had it in for her.

"I'm always telling 'er to stand up for 'erslef," said Becky, as if Clara wasn't in the room. Everyone nodded in agreement that Clara was too timid for her own good, making her squirm with embarrassment at all the attention. According to Becky, Clara's lack of gumption must have been noticed by the manager and she'd better buck her ideas up or she'd lose her job. While she was intent on berating her younger sister, she hadn't noticed that Sylvia had left her food uneaten on the plate.

Sylvia's nutritional intake and output were routinely studied and invariably found wanting by Becky. Then it would either be a trip to the doctor for a second opinion or a dose of cod liver oil. Fanny had formed her own opinion and while Becky's attention was elsewhere, she nudged her husband.

"If only Becky would give the child a little of what she likes, there'd be no problem," mouthed Fanny, "but will she listen?"

"Be quiet, she'll hear you," whispered Bob but he knew she had a point. On many occasions they'd had to endure the sight of Becky shovelling steamed white fish into Sylvia's unwilling

123

mouth, while keeping up the pretence that it was mashed potato. If Jack tried to intervene he got short shrift.

When Becky returned to the kitchen to fetch the apple pie, and was safely out of earshot, Uncle Bob pulled one of his silly faces, just to make Sylvia chuckle. He had an idea.

"Rosie, if I' 'elp yer eat yer dinner, you can 'ave some nice apple pie," he said, popping a spoonful in the little girl's mouth and another in his own, with a merry giggle. In a bid to ensure harmony reigned for the remainder of the meal, Milly and Bessie were posted as lookouts at the door, watching for Becky's return. Clara and Golda kept *schtum*, unsure whose side they should take. They knew how Becky fretted over Sylvia's unpredictable appetite, but on the other hand they didn't want to be party to a deception that could end in blame.

On the rare occasions that Becky allowed Fanny and Bob to look after Sylvia, she ate everything they provided, with crisp, hot rolls and thick butter a favourite. Fanny once made the mistake of mentioning this to Becky who took exception to the information. It wasn't unusual for her to declare she was *gefruntzled* by her relatives and take to her bed. On those occasions no amount of *schmoozing* on their part would soften her mood and without her at the helm, they were all at sixes and sevens.

While the rest of the family focused on making Sylvia's dinner disappear, Golda and Clara gazed in wonder at their little niece. "When she smiles, she's the spittin' image. It's uncanny," said Clara, with a tremble in her voice.

"Shh, Clara, don't let Becky hear you," whispered Golda, over her shoulder. "And you're upsetting me now, with that talk."

124

"I can't 'elp it. Seeing 'er, growin' up so fast, reminds me..." Clara searched her pockets for a handkerchief but finding none used her sleeve to wipe her runny nose.

When Becky returned with a tray of apple pie, everyone held their breath and Sylvia smiled her biggest smile, hoping her clean plate would bring her praise.

"She's eaten up all her fish," declared Becky in surprise. "Wait, while I fetch 'er another piece." Everyone at the table groaned, Sylvia's face crumpled, and her little finger pointed to the pie.

"Enough already with the fish, Becky," said Bob, forgetting himself, now Sylvia was crying. "Why does she drive the child bloomin' mad?" he said to Jack. Jack rolled his eyes but Becky's stern glare in Bob's direction shut down further comment. Golda hastily cut everyone a slice of pie, including Sylvia, and appreciation of Becky's pastry-making provided the necessary diversion.

The next week Becky and Jack decided to spend a little of their spare cash on professional photography. Together, they took their beloved child to a modest studio in Aldgate. The accumulated grime of the East End had left sooty deposits on the windows, and examples of the photographer's art were viewed through a film of dirt. Monochrome images of stern matriarchs, uniformed servicemen and family groups in their best clothes remained in the window, their edges deteriorating with age. Only one photograph, centrally placed, defied its humble surroundings. Jack lifted his daughter up for a better look at the image that had caught his eye.

"When you're a big girl, Sylvie, you'll be just like that lady there," he said, with his cheek pressed to hers. "All dressed up like a film star, you'll be, and everyone will ask who that beautiful lady could be."

"Will it be me?" said Sylvia. She gazed in wonder at the head and shoulders shot of a young woman with waved, bobbed hair, black chiffon and pearls at her throat, eyes bright and hopeful. "I'm going to be a lady when I grow up," she said, as if a solemn vow had been taken.

As she grew older she sometimes asked Jack if they could stop and look again at that black and white image with its promise of colour and glamour available somewhere else. In a place where no one spoke with a Cockney accent and women wore stylish, expensive clothes. Perhaps her real mother had led that kind of life. She must have been special to attract someone like her father, for whatever his faults, people said he was a very good-looking man. And that was another puzzle. Her father was a man, but everyone called him Boy.

There were so many unanswered questions about her real mother and father. In her childlike imagination they were a mysterious fairy-tale couple and she was their fairy-tale child. Perhaps her instincts were nearer to the truth than she realised for darkness invariably hovered over those time-honoured childhood tales, told at bedtime.

2

Boy
East London, 30 years earlier

He entered this world on a tide of shame and secrecy, at a time and place where illegitimacy was a lifelong disgrace.

As soon as Miriam's pregnancy became undeniable, whispered judgments about the dubious morals of the family circulated amongst East London's Dutch-Jewish community. In and around those drab streets in the summer of 1906, the impoverished native population needed little reason to despise immigrant Jews, never mind their bastard offspring. Scandal tainted them all.

As her pregnancy advanced, seventeen-year-old Miriam, the eldest of Elizabeth's nine children, stayed in the house to avoid the stares, the sideways glances and the whispered gossip. Miriam's absence from the neighbourhood fuelled further speculation from the neighbours, as they hung out their washing in the backyard.

"Hannah? Have you heard about Elizabeth's girl?" whispered one, through a hole in the brick wall. "They say it's twins she's having!"

Her neighbour let out a cry. *"Oy, gevalt!* Terrible! Twins! A double disaster I wouldn't wish on my worst enemy. We can only pray for her mother's strength."

Elizabeth's strength was never in doubt. She and her husband Samuel would survive the shame somehow. Miriam, on the other hand would have to fend for herself. What was done was done.

Miriam's harshest critic was her younger sister, Becky who vowed to shun her for life. Miriam turned her anger inward, to her unborn twins and the cause of her ruin. When her time came, and she was quietly removed to a home for 'fallen women', secrecy surrounded the birth.

No one could explain why the little girl died, but at eight weeks, the death was thought to be nature's way. Miriam's fragile state of mind prevented her from bonding with her surviving son, so it was left to his grandmother, Elizabeth to bring him up. Miriam eventually married, moved away and produced nine more children but never acknowledged her first-born son.

Everyone called the baby 'Boy', a term of affection coined by his grandmother to reflect his status as the youngest of her large brood, but Boy he remained for the rest of his life.

As a baby he slept in the same care-worn basket that had come to symbolise Elizabeth and Samuel's failed attempts to emigrate to America. Each time Elizabeth picked Boy up to soothe his cries she was back in steerage, the lowest of the low, segregated from the other passengers and forbidden to go up on deck. No escape from the acrid smells of human waste and unwashed bodies, the howling children, adults praying and cursing in Russian, Yiddish, Dutch and Polish, the horror of rough seas and always the dreadful motion sickness. Sleeping, eating and living in dark, cramped spaces, shared with hundreds of others for weeks on end. Another immigrant family travelling in hope, with dreams that they could work their way out of poverty in a different place.

When Boy grizzled and squirmed in her arms, Elizabeth recalled the strain of soothing sick children on those journeys and the humiliation on arrival of being minutely examined and questioned for signs of disease. Only on the first journey did she and Samuel travel as a couple, but she was already pregnant with Miriam by then. Becky and Clara were also born in America. Maybe if she hadn't insisted that they return to East London things might have turned out differently for Miriam.

In the end, when work dried up, life over there was no better than the one they'd left, but maybe they'd both been naïve to think that returning to East London would be better for them all in the long run. Now there were five more children to worry about, and Boy made six. Perhaps she should have paid more attention to Miriam, but she could make amends by taking care of Boy.

He was a beautiful looking infant with a shock of dark hair and enormous blue eyes. Elizabeth picked him up, cradled him gently in her arms, and looked deep and hard into those blue, blue eyes, as one-year-old Golda pulled at her skirt in protest. From a few weeks old he always held his little clenched fists close to his chest, jaw set and tiny body alert, like a boxer ready for a bout in the ring.

"That's right, Boy. You stay strong and ready to fight for what you want in this life, because nothing will come easy for you," she murmured.

In bringing him up as her son, Elizabeth knew she would have to be Boy's shield against a world that despised him. To her own children he was regarded as their troublesome youngest brother, rather than the nephew he actually was.

Boy was a wilful child with a reputation for spoiling a good thing with secrets and lies. Elizabeth put it down to the unfortunate start he'd had in life, but the uncles and aunts, masquerading as his siblings, weren't always so generous. Elizabeth somehow understood that rejection by his mother had left Boy vulnerable.

He grew into a fearless, aggressive adolescent, using his good looks and gift of the gab to invent a more appealing heritage for himself. Perhaps the sound of children singing the traditional nursery rhyme, *Oranges and Lemons* stirred something deep within his psyche. The playground singing game, mimicking the pealing church bells within the City of London, was every Cockney child's birthright, telling them what they were, whilst hinting at betterment, this year, next year, sometime, never.

'*When will you pay me, say the bells of Old Bailey,*

When I grow rich, say the bells of Shoreditch,

Pray when will that be? say the bells of Stepney,

I do not know, says the great bell of Bow'.

If he stuck to the tale that his father was a rich Australian farmer, let anyone dare to say it wasn't so!

The neighbourhood children liked to taunt him with his own tall tales when his boasting got under their skin. In scraps with his peers he knew he could always count on his beloved grandmother to take his side if push came to shove.

He bullied smaller kids to hand over their sweets or pennies. Sometimes he paid with a black eye, as some of the victims had bigger brothers and cousins, but he had the occasional triumph too. One day six relatives of his latest victim cornered him on the way back from school.

"Oi, Boy, where's ya kangaroo? Ain't yer dad sent it over yet? Fort you said e' was a rich bloke, wiv his own farm," said the tallest, with a sneer that made his companions grin.

Boy tensed, looked from face to face, curling his lip in contempt. He pushed his cap back, eyeing the ringleader with hate. "What's it to you?" he countered, spitting on the pavement.

"Whoever 'eard of Jews being farmers anyway," said another, laughing, "they're only interested in countin' their money."

"I'd hate to be a bastard," said the ringleader, grinning at his audience of sympathisers. "What happened, Boy, didn't Daddy want yer?" Boy's right-handed punch landed just as he looked away, sending the speaker sprawling face first into the gutter, so his bottom lip, oozing blood, was also liberally seasoned with grit.

Clip-clopping by on the other side of the road, the rag and bone man's blinkered horse paid no attention but the driver, whose call for scrap metal and rags was interrupted by the altercation, watched as Boy kicked his way clear of his enemies and made a run for it down the street.

"Scalliwags, the lot of them. Need their ears boxed," he muttered, flicking the horse's reigns in annoyance.

Another time Boy almost got caught red-handed in the market with an old woman's purse. She'd left her shopping bag open and was looking in the other direction. He dropped it further up the road when he heard her shouting for the police. But it was a close shave and word got around that he was a thief.

His conscience troubled him, though when Elizabeth confronted him about the missing change she'd left on the mantelpiece for the gas.

"I never took no money," he said, a little too quickly.

"Don't you lie to me," she said, shaking him by the shoulders. "Look me in the eye, Boy..." her voice tailed off as he protested his innocence once more. He saw what he'd become in her tears and he hated himself. He put his head on her shoulder and she embraced him.

Only with her arms tight around him did he feel secure enough in her love to confess. "I dunno why I did it. I'll make it up to you one day, I will." He meant what he said but he didn't know how to make it happen.

School was of little interest to him but it was another blow when his headmaster declined to give him a report when he left, predicting that the fourteen-year old would have to make his way in the world by living on his wits. Boy was smart and articulate but money was tight, and the family wondered how he would be able to contribute to the household, or make any sort of a living without a school report to give to an employer. They all hoped, for their mother's sake, that he would mend his ways before it was too late. Meanwhile he'd talked his way into the billiard halls and illegal gambling clubs around Mile End with a proposition that appealed to the shady characters that ran them. He'd find gullible punters on the street, and for a small commission from the club, persuade them in. He enjoyed the challenge and the attention, but his aunts and uncles feared it was only a matter of time before the police knocked on their door.

Some of Elizabeth's children had growing families of their own but they continued to live in the rented rooms they grew up in, sharing what they had and helping each other out as best they could. That was the way amongst the East End Jewish community. They were all poor, but together the family created a safety net to ensure that no one went hungry. It often involved having more than one job, or whatever it took to avoid the indignity of applying to the Jewish Board of Guardians for nourishment, courtesy of the soup kitchen.

Perhaps a local gang bribed the police to turn a blind eye, or Boy was exceptionally agile. One way or another he managed to dodge arrest when they raided the gambling clubs. He could have been recruited into the East End's criminal fraternity permanently if his Uncle Ruby hadn't had a bright idea.

Uncle Ruby worked as a machinist in a tailor's workshop through the week but had found a way to make a bit extra on a Sunday by joining the market traders in and round 'the Lane'. Petticoat Lane was a good place to sell 'cribs,' the offcuts of cloth left over from a larger job. It was more profitable than selling the cloth to a rag merchant for a few pennies and there was also the chance of picking up an order for the workshop for the following week, to keep the boss sweet. Takings had taken a dive at the market lately so Ruby enlisted Boy's help. If Boy did most of the talking, he reasoned, they might attract a bigger crowd. A little extra Sunday job would keep the lad out of trouble and with his good looks, he'd be better at getting the attention of the female customers. Ruby outlined the idea to Elizabeth and the rest of the family, and they all signalled their approval.

Lured by the prospect of a little extra cash, and a platform that played to his strengths, Boy was happy to oblige.

Standing on a wooden crate, he had presence, the vocal force required to be heard above all the other hubbub in the market, and the blue-eyed patter to engage potential customers. Ruby tended to stammer when he was nervous which wasn't good for sales.

"Ladies, gather round, gather round," Boy began. "Come and see what bargains we 'ave for you today. Oh, my word, such an array of cloth in all colours and," nodding at a blushing Ruby, "a master tailor here an 'all to take down your orders. Prices, madam? Lemme tell you now, we are positively givin' it away today, but we won't be here tomorrow, so let's get down to business."

A few elderly women stopped to listen, nudging each other and nodding in Boy's direction. Ruby had tipped out a jumble of assorted samples onto a makeshift table and silently beckoned the women to start rummaging while Boy was giving his spiel. The sight of a few turning over the goods always encouraged more to join in.

"That's right, ladies," said Boy, "no charge for feeling the quality, we're not here to waste your time with *schmutters*. Only the best tweeds, twills and flannels. Saville Row, we are, right here in the Lane, but only today, mind."

Boy was just warming to his theme when he noticed two young women hovering at the back of the small crowd. He stepped up the performance a notch, hoping to keep their attention.

"Bespoke tailoring, available here, and collect next week. Plenty 'ere for your old man's new trousers madam, and prices

134

guaranteed to put a smile on your face, or I'm a Chinaman," he said, with his eyes trained on the two girls. He noticed they'd moved a little closer and one of them, the fair-skinned one, with the brown cloche hat was looking in his direction.

The girls were obviously sisters. Their striking good looks, the same but different. Night and Day. The taller of the two, had dark curls and soulful brown eyes and the smaller, her fair-skinned, blue-eyed, counterpart.

The patter was working like a dream and a crowd gathered around Ruby's stall, some with money and cloth in hand. While Boy's attention was taken up with the first round of sales, he didn't notice the two girls move away and along the street. Just as they reached the corner, the smaller of the two seemed to hold back. While her taller sister stopped to chat to an acquaintance, she turned, blue eyes scanning the crowd for a glimpse of the cheeky cloth seller, but there were too many people in the way.

3

1925

The crowds were drifting away from the market and Harry was chilled to the bone. He stamped his feet and rubbed his palms together to bring the circulation back. He could see Boy, his helper for the morning, wandering up the street, finding out how business had gone at other stalls. Harry put two fingers in his mouth and whistled in his direction. Boy turned and put one thumb in the air, signalling he was on his way back. They hadn't had a bad day between them, but it was time they packed up the stock.

Boy made quick work of moving Harry's unsold boots from the makeshift stall back to the barrow. The older man looked on as the youngster's deft movements made light of the task, prompting thoughts about his great loss all those years ago. Sam might have been his helper on days like these. Stillborn. He would have been twenty today. The same age as Boy.

"There you are. All done 'Arry," said Boy, jolting Harry back to the present.

"God bless," he said, his eyes full of tears. "Take this and 'ave a bet on the gee-gees," he said, slipping some silver into Boy's pocket. He knew the lad enjoyed a flutter.

"Cheers, 'Arry. You alright?" said Boy, concerned by the old man's show of emotion, but with a more pressing question on his mind.

At this point, a few weeks had gone by since Boy had spotted the two girls in the crowd. He'd been hoping they'd make another appearance but there'd been no sign of them on a Sunday or any other day. Perhaps the cold weather had put them off. You never knew what a cough and cold might turn into at this time of year. and the Lane wasn't the most salubrious of places. The younger one had a beautiful smile. He'd like to see that smile again. It was a long shot, but worth asking. Harry knew everyone.

"Just before you go, 'Arry," said Boy, touching the older man on the arm, "you wouldn't 'appen to know two girls, so alike, they have to be sisters. The spittin' image of each other, one dark, the other fair. Ring a bell wiv you at all?"

Harry thought for a moment, and then realisation dawned.

"You must mean Hetty and Rose. Lovely girls. My Minnie knows the family, helped with the catering when Hetty got married last year. Their mother has relatives in Canada, so they tried their luck there for a few years but couldn't settle. Changed their name when they came back to London. Couldn't be proper English with the Dutch name they had, a right mouthful it was," he added, with a gap-toothed grin.

Boy knew it was common practice to anglicise a foreign name to save the embarrassment of spelling it out to bigoted officials. An obviously Jewish name might also risk alienating potential non-Jewish employers. One of his own uncles, stubbornly insisted on pronouncing his surname differently from the rest of the family because he thought it sounded more English. Or maybe

137

it was an attempt to distance himself from the family. Either way it seemed to make no difference to his fortunes.

"But the other sister, the smaller, fairer one? "Rose, did you say?" The casual tone Boy was aiming for had been forgotten and Harry's kind brown eyes looking into his, made him feel uncomfortably self-conscious.

Harry patted Boy's shoulder. He shrugged off Harry's hand without really meaning to. He longed for affection but didn't always know how to receive it. The older man turned to go, sensing he'd overstepped an unspoken mark. "I 'eard she works in the cigarette factory on Whitechapel Road," he said, over his shoulder.

"Does she?" said Boy, his tone signalling gratitude for the information. "See yer next week, look after yerself," but Harry hadn't heard. He was already on his way, arthritic fingers gripping the barrow handles for support as he made his way slowly up the street.

Later, back at home, when everyone else was in bed and the house was quiet, Boy sat by the fire, dreaming how the family would rejoice if he could tell them he'd found a special girl. Instead of the resigned sighs and doubtful looks that usually came his way, they'd be butting in and talking over each other, animated with excitement, shouting *Mazeltov* so loudly the neighbours would all come running to see what the fuss was about. They'd all be asking him about the girl, eyes bright with anticipation. The news would pass from one to the other and soon the tailors, dressmakers, milliners, bakers, caterers, barbers, jewellers, musicians, florists and indeed, anyone with a connection to the wedding business, would be anticipating the requirements and hoping to play a part in the happy couple's special day.

He knew Elizabeth's only wish was to see him settled. On more than one occasion he'd heard her telling other people that a wife would make him a *mensch*.

With a wife, he'd be somebody.

4

Rose
1928

L ily Turner, the workshop supervisor looked across the room with affection and pride. It was almost 5.30pm but the six young women at the tobacco rolling tables were hard workers and usually had to be prompted to stop for the day.

Mechanisation hadn't yet come to the smaller enterprises but it was changing the way cigarettes were produced at the big factories, and Lily wasn't in favour of it. The idea that her girls, with hand rolling skills passed down from their fathers — Dutch cigar makers all — might only be required to pack the machine-made products into boxes, was unthinkable.

Every morning Rose and her colleagues lined up with their trays to collect handfuls of beaten tobacco leaves from the delivery box. At their tables, they stored the tobacco under a damp cloth, pressing it flat with a small roller. Placing a single cigarette paper on a square board, the experienced maker's fingers could judge the exact amount of tobacco required for one cigarette. The unruly strands were pulled from underneath the cloth, carefully laid along the length of the paper and rolled into shape on the board. The most delicate part of the operation was applying just the right amount of paste to seal the paper. When nine or ten cigarettes were ready, the maker aligned the ends for simultaneous trimming with a pair of small shears.

Lily's job was to total the workshop's daily output and arrange collection and delivery to the packing department. Looking up from her desk by the window, she smiled to herself when she spotted a familiar figure patiently waiting on the opposite side of the street, outside the entrance to the Pavilion Theatre.

"Rose, your young man's here again," she called, "as 'andsome as ever."

Rose looked up from her work when she heard her name. Brushing stray strands of tobacco from her fingers, she hurried to the window. A tram blocked her view but as it went on its way she saw him, framed in the theatre's doorway, eyes trained on the entrance to her building. He was there, just as he said he would be on the days when there was no meeting. Greyhound racing had arrived in East London and working people were embracing this new form of entertainment in their droves. 'Going to the dogs' to see six, lean hounds, chase a mechanical hare around a sandy track had given Boy a route to a legitimate occupation, at just the right time. If he wanted a wife, he needed a credible future.

He'd started as runner, handling the cash between client and bookmaker and proving he was trustworthy. Now he was a tic tac man at the dog track, signalling the odds and taking the punter's bets. Rose had been to a meeting and seen him direct the racegoers to hand over fistfuls of money, using a mysterious language of calls and hand signs.

"Take your apron off and go! What are you waiting for?" said Lily, with an encouraging smile.

"Ooh, I don't know. Yes. I must hurry, and now I'm all fingers and thumbs, undoing this apron," said Rose, laughing at herself.

"Rosie that's the third time this week. How romantic!" called Betty, with a sigh from her bench, prompting smiles and nods from the other girls. Betty had resigned herself to staying single. Her left eye turned inwards, and her mother liked to remind everyone that a defect like that ruined her chances with men.

Rose lifted her coat from the hook in the hall and pulling a soft felt hat from a pocket, she called out good night to her colleagues, before making her way downstairs to the street.

A year had a gone by since he'd first tipped his cap to her on a Friday night in the Mile End Road. The pavement was crowded with groups of single young men and women, looking for romance. She recognised him from the market straightaway and the sight of him made her heart beat a little faster. The next week they stopped to talk as her companions strolled slowly ahead. She told him she worked at the cigarette factory. Only a small firm, opposite the Palace but he already knew as much. Something about the warmth of her response told him to be bolder.

A few days later, he turned up outside as she left for the day. "I 'ope you don't mind," he said, twisting his cap in his hand, "but I was 'oping you'd let me walk you 'ome." The request was so endearing, almost childlike. When she looked in his eyes, she only saw the man he wanted to be.

Now he waited outside for her whenever he could. And when he wasn't there, she dawdled, looking up and down the street, just in case they'd somehow missed each other, and he was running to catch her up. It was on those walks together, along Whitechapel High Street and the Mile End Road that they fell in love.

He preferred to talk about her, rather than himself. Her family background was less complicated than his and more conventional. Two parents and an older sister, married, with a baby boy. Grandparents that emigrated from Holland to Canada. No secrets to explain. He was happy to listen as she chattered away, explaining how her family made several trips to Canada by steamship.

"We still went third class, mind you, but it wasn't like in the old days, when your *bubba* sailed to America. It was all modern when we went. We had a cabin and proper food on china plates. I was only young of course, but I can still remember the names of the ships," she said. "Laurentic, Megantic, Teutonic and Virginia." She recited the names like the eight-year old she was when she learned them. "I loved the sounds of those names. I used to write them down, over and over in a little book to learn the spelling. Steamships on the White Star Line. So funny what you remember, isn't it?"

Boy stopped, unhooked his arm from hers, put his hands on her shoulders, and looked deep into her questioning eyes. His hand gently brushed her cheek. She was a dainty girl and there was a fragility about her that made him fearful.

She searched his face for clues. "What's wrong? Have I said something to upset you? You look so serious."

He struggled to find the right words.

"It's just that...well it upsets me to think. ... what if you'd never come back?" He looked bereft at the mere thought.

"Let's not think about what ifs. We might have stayed I suppose, but for the war starting and..."

"That's not what I meant," he said. "Those poor souls on the Titanic expected to come back but they didn't, did they? Same owners as the ships you went on and within a year or two of your family travelling across the Atlantic."

His train of thought revealed how much he cared and there in the middle of the street, with the light fading, she threw her arms around his neck and they stayed like that, clinging to each other, neither wanting to break free.

It was November and Mile End Road was foggy and damp. Men and women were hurrying home to the warmth of their loved ones. The owner of the hardware shop on the corner was bringing in the pots and pans that hung on strings outside the door. Two children stopped to look at the buns left for sale in the baker's window, till their mother turned and called them to heel. Buses, delivery vans, horses and carts went on their way, but on the pavement, oblivious to it all, two young lovers, clung to the life they saw in each other.

He couldn't believe that a gentle girl like Rose really wanted him. He was fearful her parents, Hyman and Jane would disapprove but any doubts they had were kept strictly between themselves. "A tic tac man? What sort of job is this for a Jewish boy? Better, he should have a trade," said Hyman. Hetty, his elder daughter had married a hotel chef. Long hours but a respectable occupation and regular money.

"He's a lovely looking young man and if he earns a living and enough to keep them both, who are we to say? He's certainly smart. He'll have his own business in a few years, you'll see," said Jane.

Boy saw his relations as brash and confrontational in comparison and there were so many of them, but they held their tongues in her presence and the encouraging looks they gave him suggested he'd moved up in their estimation now he had her on his arm.

Importantly, the match had Elizabeth's approval. By bringing Rose into the family he'd done something right at last. Out of earshot of Elizabeth, a few doubters amongst her children worried if trouble lay ahead, now a date had been set for the wedding.

"How can Boy understand the responsibilities that go with marriage?" said his Uncle Ruby.

"You know she's a year older than him?" ventured Becky.

"Really? Unusual, ach, but such a lovely girl. Maybe it's a good thing, the age difference. Let's hope for the best," said Uncle Bob.

So it was, on July 21, 1929, the groom, a racecourse tipster and the bride, a cigarette maker, stood together under the canopy at Sandys Row, the Dutch community's synagogue, near Brick Lane, Spitalfields.

A few guests noticed that the groom's second-hand jacket had seen better days, but most agreed that a gentleman's top hat, white gloves and two-tone brogues gave him the look of a proper gentleman.

The groom's good looks and sense of style did not go unnoticed by Eva, a cousin on the bride's side. "Pity about the rest of his family. Not one of them dressed for the occasion. A right lot of ragamuffins," she murmured to an elderly aunt.

As the familiar rituals played out, the mother of the bride and the groom's grandmother gushed with pride and delight. Rose in dainty Juliet cap, handkerchief point dress and lace veil, circled her groom seven times, a symbol of how she surrounds and protects him with love. Blessings were said as the couple shared wine, before the sound of glass shattering beneath the groom's shoe, prompted every guest to shout, "*Mazeltov!*"

Rabbis offer different interpretations for the significance of breaking a glass. Some will joke that it's the last chance the groom has to put his foot down. Others say that it's a reminder that even in times of joy, life brings sadness and sorrow, that life itself is as fragile as glass and that the couple should enjoy every day together as if it were their last. And there are even those who suggest that the sound of breaking glass scares away the evil spirits that would spit venom on a happy occasion for their own amusement.

High on happiness, the newlyweds moved into two ground floor rooms in the house in Copley Street, Stepney Green that Boy had grown up in.

The next weekend they treated themselves to a honeymooner's day trip to the coast, mingling with the other pleasure seekers strolling along the pier in the sunshine. On a bench at the seafront they fed each other cockles and whelks, doused in vinegar, and in the gardens, joined in the singalong as the band played *Makin' Whoopee'*, the hit on everyone's lips that year.

"Come on the roller coaster, with me, Rose," said Boy. He knew she wasn't keen on heights, and he hoped the distant screams from the diving, looping passengers wouldn't put her off.

"If we must, but you know I'll scream my head off and then you'll wish you hadn't got me on it," she said, kissing him on the cheek.

Holding onto their hats with one hand and the rail in front with the other, they both screamed in fear and excitement till the most daring of all the pleasure rides at the funfair came to a sudden halt and it was all over. Almost time to take the train back to London.

They walked back, past the haunted house where earlier in the day, their distorted reflections had made them laugh till they cried.

"Oh look, we missed that ride at the end," said Rose, pointing up ahead, past the turning to the train station. "We've got time for the ghost train, haven't we?" she asked, pulling him towards the booth where tickets were sold.

He couldn't refuse her anything.

"Two please," he said at the window. The woman in the booth, took the money, jerking her head towards the track and the open carriage waiting in front of the closed doors.

"Hold me tight, now," said Rose climbing in beside Boy. "I've heard, they can suddenly wave things in your face to make you jump, and I might fall out with the shock of it," she said, with laughter in her voice.

"Nah, it'll be nuffin' but a bit of thread that feels like a cobweb, and someone making noises with a sheet over their 'eads. Ooh, we're off," said Boy, drawing her closer to him.

The solitary carriage lurched forward. The doors swung open with a metallic scream and the couple disappeared into a musty, black beyond. The ghost train was always a dark ride and the clock was ticking on the journey they'd begun.

5

Rose conceived two months after their wedding. As the weeks went by and the characteristic symptoms persisted, it was Hetty who noticed the change in her younger sister first. Rose hadn't dared to hope.

"I know you're expecting," said Hetty, "it's a subtle thing, but you just look different to me."

Rose only allowed herself to believe it when Boy began to wonder if his wife's nausea and the overwhelming tiredness had an obvious explanation.

"I'm worried about you," he said, pulling her close. "If you're really expecting, I should be taking more care of you – and the little surprise, you've given me," he added.

"We'll be a proper family soon," she said, trying to allay his shock. "Hetty has the boys and we'll have the girls," she laughed. Hetty had given birth to her second son a few months before. Good news must be infectious, they joked. The children in the family would all grow up together. Rose always saw the bright side. Boy loved her for that.

When she felt the first fluttering movements, Nellie Dunn, the local midwife confirmed everyone's hopes. A baby was on the way.

"Don't worry too much about the swelling in your fingers and ankles. It'll soon go when baby arrives," said Nellie. "Put your feet up and rest a little more."

Her mother and Hetty had said much the same thing, but Rose's ankles remained puffy and her wedding ring tight. Reluctantly, she removed the ring while she still could.

Now that she'd stopped working, Boy was spending more time at the racecourse and at other odd jobs he'd picked up.

"Just a few favours for a friend to keep the wolf from the door," he told her.

Hetty, her mother and Boy's aunts took charge in the long hours he spent out of the house. The door to the street was always left open. Nourishing chicken soup was in plentiful supply, and the women up and down the street rallied round as her time was getting close.

The pains started in the morning, shortly after Boy left the house for the day. Hetty let herself in and discovered Rose bent over in pain, gripping the back of a chair in the kitchen. She gently guided her sister back to the bedroom and began to note the time between contractions. The baby wasn't due for another month.

When a neighbour went to fetch Nellie Dunn a few hours later, the midwife welcomed the news.

"Early or not, this baby needs to come," she told herself, reaching for her bag. She'd seen this before. Delivery of the baby was the best cure. She'd noted the raised blood pressure and albumin trace present in the urine a few days before. She'd planned to return later in the week in case headaches or sickness developed. That would have been a warning sign.

Progress was fast, pitching an undersized girl into the world on a wing and a prayer. One that needed her first breath to be gently blown into her tiny lungs before she found her own voice. That small, urgent cry, bringing joy and relief to mother, midwife and family members, was finally heard in that home on the afternoon of 10 May 1930.

The dangers were being checked off. The placenta, examined, was complete. The new mother, shocked and exhausted, sipped on a cup of sweet tea.

Boy couldn't be located when Nellie broke the news to the waiting relatives. When he eventually headed for home, a few pounds up from a win on the horses, several of the neighbours greeted him on the street to tell him he was a father.

"A little girl! *Mazeltov* to you both!" said Yetta.

"It was all very quick, you know," warned Dora, "She'll need time to recover."

"Tell her Morry and Minnie send their love, won't you?"

"What are you calling her? God bless, from all of us at number 21," from another. He couldn't take it all in.

Both sides of the family had gathered at the house. On his return, they greeted him in turn, each with joy in their eyes and love in their hearts. Only Hetty hung back. She spoke to him quietly, out of hearing of his relatives.

"Come and see them both with me. See if you think Rose is alright. Maybe it was the shock of it all, but she seems confused," she said. A sudden cry and the crash of broken glass from the bedroom interrupted the speculation.

They burst in and found Rose in the corner of the room, vomiting into a bucket, a shattered glass at her feet.

"Rose, it's me and Boy is here now. Come back to bed," said Hetty.

She looked at them both with a wild expression, but let herself be guided, one on each arm. Her face appeared swollen.

"My head," she whispered.

"Call an ambulance, Boy," said Hetty. "The midwife said if she wakes with a headache it's an emergency."

He bolted from the room at the instruction, his daughter's head cradled awkwardly in the crook of his arm.

"It'll be alright, Rose," said Hetty, mopping her sister's head, with a damp flannel, "the ambulance is on its way and they'll take you to the hospital."

Rose studied her sister's face.

"That's good. You see, I'm having a baby, soon," she murmured.

In the next room, Boy instinctively handed the baby to Becky. No words were spoken. He had to be with Rose, until the danger had passed. Becky knew what to do with babies.

The neighbours came out onto the street when the ambulance arrived and a few watched as she was carried out of the house, unconscious. Boy stepped in behind and the doors closed. From the pavement, the neighbours watched until the ambulance turned the corner.

"The East End's top maternity place," said Dora to her sister. "She'll be alright, there, please God."

"Just a precaution," added Yetta, as the other neighbours speculated on the need for an ambulance.

Throughout the journey, while Boy held Rose's frail hand, his faith in the medical experts remained absolute but he was an

151

innocent in a world he couldn't comprehend. Adjustment to the new reality was swift and harsh.

He had to wait outside the room while the nurses made the necessary preparations. When he was finally admitted, the sight of her, secured to a padded bed in a darkened room, was horrific. The sister on duty saw his shock and explained that this was necessary to ensure the patient did not injure themselves in the event of a seizure. He was told he could sit by her bed and talk to her gently but she may not respond.

"It's important that she has complete bed rest and we are helping her to do that," said the nurse. "That's what the doctor meant when he spoke to you about medical sedation." Boy nodded as if he understood but there was so much to take in, the doctor's words were like a foreign language. A serious condition. Observations every twenty minutes. That's something he remembered the doctor saying. All night, and through the day they would check she was alright.

There were short periods when she was restless, not quite asleep but not fully awake either. Boy would hear her groan, as if she was having a bad dream and then fall silent again. Perhaps she could still hear his voice, even if she appeared to be unconscious.

"Rose, it's me. I'm 'ere with you," he said, squeezing her hand. "You can 'ear me, I know you can. Don't worry about the baby, she's"... His words petered out. The thought of a baby, their baby, needing its mother was too painful. He swallowed hard and tried again when he saw her eyelids flutter.

"When you're better we'll go away. To the coast. You'll like that. The sea air will do you good. Remember when we went for the day for our 'oneymoon? We'll take the little one this time. Don't leave me, Rose. I love you and I don't know 'ow to carry on without you." He wiped the tears from his eyes and gently caressed her cheek.

He kept a vigil by her bed until exhausted, he gave in to sleep for a few minutes. The next thing he knew he was woken by a nurse. The doctor was doing his rounds. He would have to wait outside.

When he was allowed back in he read the notes at the foot of her bed, searching for explanations in the columns of strange words. Magnesium sulphate, calcium glucosate, stomach and colon washes. Blood pressure, systolic, diastolic, always too high, pulse racing, temperature rising, albumin present in urine. What did it all mean and when could she come home?

The fits started on the second day. The nurse was completing her observations when Boy saw a strange movement on one side of Rose's face, an unnatural twitching of the muscle. The nurse saw it too and ran from the room to alert colleagues. Rose opened her eyes, but only the whites were visible. Boy ran from the room, screaming for help. Four nurses ran in.

He paced the floor outside, terrified at what he'd seen, but was spared the rest. Violent contractions of her body followed, her arms visibly rigid and held above throughout. As if her whole being was possessed by a merciless demon, her torso rose from the bed in a hideous curve. The nurses had to use all their strength to keep her still, to stop her swallowing her tongue or breaking a limb, amid the rapid, uncontrollable spasms. Two and half minutes of this agony continued before it passed, and she was still again. Several more episodes followed and in between them she fell back to sleep.

On the third morning, as Boy stroked her head she opened her eyes and asked where she was.

"Oh, fank God!" he cried. "You're in' ospital. I've been 'ere all the time, Rose," said Boy, close to tears, this time with gratitude, that she had woken at last.

"Bring the baby," she whispered.

Within the hour Boy took the sleeping infant from Becky's arms at the hospital entrance. Becky reminded him to keep the blanket tucked tight around the newborn.

"We'll be back, 'ome soon," he told her. "She's getting better and this'll help,"

He returned to Rose and placed their daughter in her arms.

"I'm naming you Sylvia," said Rose, gazing into her daughter's blue eyes as if the baby herself had asked what she was called. She stared hard at the tiny face as the nurse completed her notes and left the room. "I've given my life for you, but now I'm letting you go. Please take her," she said to Boy.

The baby lay in the hospital crib at the side of the bed. Rose lay back on the pillow and closed her eyes, beads of sweat starting to form on her forehead. As the convulsion began, Boy cried out for help.

Her body's internal chaos directed the terror for the last time. Both her eyes remained wide open, as if in disbelief. Before capitulation, there was a desperate rasping in the throat and foaming, bloodied saliva visible at her mouth. An emergency team tried in vain to revive her but defeated, they stood in silence by the bed, heads lowered as the small stirrings and trembling cries of a hungry baby filled the room.

Later that day the patient's notes were updated for the last time. In red ink. Red for the ones that didn't go home.

6

Boy stood on the hospital steps, paralysed by grief, his baby daughter in his arms, and a death certificate in his pocket.

Feelings that took him right back to the jeers and disgraces of childhood had surfaced anew. All those years when he'd felt bewildered, angry, and abandoned, it was Elizabeth's devotion that had saved him. Then he met Rose. Now she was gone and nothing about his world made sense anymore.

Weeping, he looked at the sleeping baby, but the tears he shed were for himself and the happiness that had been snatched away from him so cruelly. How had it come to this? They'd hadn't even celebrated their first wedding anniversary.

The responsibility of being the sole provider of care and protection to this helpless creature was overwhelming. What was he supposed to do with a baby and no wife? He'd said as much to the doctor. Much of the medical explanation had gone over his head. Not understanding the words made it harder to accept.

They'd asked for his occupation to fill in the details on the death certificate and he couldn't bring himself to say he was a racecourse tipster. Boot salesman sounded more respectable and it was sort of half true, if he counted helping old Harry out in the market.

The broken faces, the sobbing of his aunts and uncles, his in-laws, and her beloved sister would haunt him for evermore. Post-partum eclampsia the death certificate said. Something to do with high blood pressure after the birth. Caused a seizure. None of it mattered now.

Something the nurse said kept playing back in his mind, though.

"She's a little small, but she's a miracle and such a comfort in your terrible loss."

He'd nodded absently at the time. He'd always thought doctors could choose whose life was saved.

A distant clock struck the hour, and he realised he was still trying to process the events of the last few days from the hospital steps.

He stared down at the tiny form that had brought such joy only three days earlier. Now he looked at her with coldness in his heart.

"Why her and not you," he hissed, and then he wept again at his callousness. His own mother must have resented his birth too and now history had come full circle. Someone else would have to rescue this baby, as he had been rescued.

He stepped purposefully down the steps and headed for home.

It was a short walk back from the hospital on Whitechapel Road to Copley Street and Boy kept his eyes fixed ahead. He wouldn't think about the countless times they'd walked and embraced on this street. The shopkeepers going about their daily routines stopped, took off their caps and bowed their heads as he walked by. A group of chattering women on the corner fell silent as he approached. At the sight of him carrying his baby, one covered her face with her hands and wept loudly.

Like a prayer, they murmured as one, the Jewish line of comfort to the bereaved, "Wishing you long life."

From another, "God bless. Such a tragedy."

He didn't acknowledge them. After the funeral, and in view of the circumstances, there would be seven days of ritual observance for prayers and comfort. Seated on low stools he would receive their condolences then, alongside Rose's immediate family.

He feared breaking down if he stopped to explain, but then a little girl with jam round her mouth stood in his path, questions on her lips. "Is that your baby mister? Can I have a look?"

"Not now, dear," he said, sidestepping the child and quickening his pace.

"Why? Is her Mummy going to feed her?" she called to his retreating back.

He reached the house and let himself in. When he opened the door to the rarely used front parlour, the aunts and uncles all rose to their feet, shock etched on their faces. The men, unshaven, hollow-eyed, the women, pale and unkempt. No one spoke.

They watched in silence as Boy gently lay the sleeping baby down on the old sofa. In position, they formed a grotesque tableau, every eye trained on the tiny swaddled shape.

They'd discussed a solution just before he arrived. The unmarried aunts dabbed at their eyes, knowing they could offer little. Those that had families of their own were already struggling. Money was tight, and they could do without another mouth to feed. There was only one sensible way forward, and they hoped Boy would agree to it.

Finally, he broke the silence. "I don't know what to do," he said, waving his hands towards the baby in despair.

They moved in a protective circle around him. Only Becky and her husband Jack stayed in their places, staring down at the baby in awe. They'd been married for some years but had no children of their own. Becky could always be relied on to feed and care for the children in the family when required, but she saw something different in this baby than in the others she'd looked after. This one could be hers and hers alone, a precious possession to keep, protect, and shield from the whole world.

"We'll help you, Boy," she said without looking up. "We'll take care of her. She won't want for anything, we'll make sure of that, the little darlin'."

"She's so beautiful," said Jack, his voice wavering. "Would you let us bring her up?" To him, this baby was a perfect being, one he could shower with love and all the material things he could afford. She would be his pride and joy and the friend he would have for the rest of his life.

One of the uncles chimed in. "What do you say, Boy? It's the best way, don't you think?"

Everyone held their breath, waiting for his response, trying to read his face. The baby let out a little cry in her sleep.

"Thank you, Becky and Jack," he said at last. "I don't know how I will ever thank you enough, but I'll pay for everything you need to look after her. And more. On my life, I swear I won't let her be a burden to you, Becky, I promise."

Some of the aunts and uncles exchanged relieved looks.

The baby began to cry. Becky lifted her from the sofa and held her close.

When Boy saw his daughter in the arms of another he knew something was being taken from him that was rightfully his. Becky knew it too. She didn't trust Boy and she didn't want his promises. With promises came interference and the possibility that one day he might change his mind and take the baby away from her. Or worse still, when the child grew up she would want to be with her own father.

Jack knew that if the child loved him, she wouldn't want to leave him but nevertheless, a bargain was struck to safeguard everyone's interests.

Becky and Jack would bring the baby up as their own, but out of respect to her father she would keep his surname. Sylvia was the name she'd been given, but within the family she would also be known as Rose, in memory of her mother. Boy would have access to his daughter whenever he wanted, but an official adoption should take place as soon as possible. It was settled. Becky and Jack had a child of their own at last.

Boy slipped out of the parlour and opened the door to the bedroom he and Rose had shared. Taking a deep breath, he stepped inside for the last time. The bed was unmade, as they'd left it after the ambulance arrived. The dent in the pillow where she'd last laid her aching head was still visible. He bent to touch it tenderly, and as he did, something caught his eye. A gold wedding band, in a little dish on the table by the bed. She'd taken it off when her fingers started to swell. There was another ring there too, set with a tiny emerald. Her mother had given it to her on their wedding day. Perhaps he should ask Becky to keep it safe for now, so the baby could have something from her mother when she was older. His hand hovered over the dish as if he was torn.

160

He'd get a good price for two rings if he touted them around the jewellers he knew in Black Lion Yard. Finally, he picked up both rings, slipped them in his pocket, and left the house without a word. There was a funeral to pay for.

7

It was the Sunday following Sylvia's eighth birthday and everything about her looked scrubbed and polished. From the tip of her little black shoes to the pink satin ribbon in her glossy dark hair, she shone. While Becky fastened the buttons on the back of her new dress, Sylvia inspected her reflection. The bedroom mirror was pitted and stained so Sylvia had to twist and turn to check her outfit would impress the visitors, as Becky intended. New clothes made her feel special.

Tea, as usual would be taken in the front parlour and the cups and plates had already been taken through. The door to the seldom used room had been left open all morning but a stale, unlived-in odour still lingered in there.

Once a month, Boy, accompanied by his second wife, spent an awkward hour or so in this room, for the purpose of maintaining contact with his eldest daughter. Two years after Rose's death, he'd married her cousin, Eva and they had two daughters of their own. Betsy aged six and Jenny, four, looked forward to seeing their elder stepsister.

There was no doubt that everyone found Boy's second marriage hard to accept. The speed with which it happened following Rose's death was especially hard for her parents, who were hit by a second tragedy when their elder daughter Hetty, mother to two small boys, contracted tuberculosis. After Hetty's death, and his second marriage, Boy was estranged from his first wife's family for good.

His aunts and uncles loved Rose and when Eva came on the scene the reaction towards her was hostile, the motives, suspicious.

"She had her eye on 'im from the start and then she pounced," declared Clara, who rarely spoke ill of anyone.

In truth, Eva was a little ahead of her time for the aunts and uncles to cope with. She wasn't in the least bit intimidated by what anyone in the family thought of her. On the contrary, she revelled in creating a stir. She wore trousers for one thing, which Becky considered outrageous.

A birthday card for Sylvia, containing money, had been received a few days before their visit. A handwritten note had been slipped inside which read, *'Happy Birthday, from your loving father. PS Don't thank me for the money when I come to see you'*. Becky had sniffed at this message, muttering to Jack that the message proved Boy's wife held the purse strings and the cheek of it, begrudging a birthday gift to his own child, if thanks for it were given in her hearing.

Consequently, Becky felt the need to remind Sylvia how to behave towards her father and his wife, in case she'd forgotten. "Remember, you don't need to kiss yer father when he comes in or when 'e leaves. 'E has his own family and he don't want you as well. You have me and yer Uncle Jack. Just be polite to Eva. She's nuffing to do wiv' you, neever."

This comment harked back to the time Becky discovered a note under Sylvia's pillow in which she'd listed all the members of her family, daring to include 'my real mother, Rose' and 'my stepmother, Eva'. She had also written that her Aunt Becky and Uncle Jack loved her very much, but Becky had neglected to read that part and tore the note up, which made Sylvia feel she had said something she should be ashamed of.

When Becky went to answer the door, Sylvia stayed in the bedroom, worried she might do something else that would upset Becky, without really meaning to. Like that time when Betsy and Jenny had climbed onto Boy's lap, one on each knee and she had held out her hands to be included too, but there didn't seem to be enough room for her. On his knee and perhaps in his heart too. On that occasion Becky had noticed a perceived fondness in her small child for her father and it was pounced on afterwards, expressed in such hurt and anguished tones that Sylvia had felt overwhelmed with guilt and shame for her mistake. Becky always hovered somewhere near after that during these visits, as if to make sure there was no repetition.

As she heard the visitors being ushered into the parlour, Sylvia crept down the corridor and sat on the stairs. She heard Becky and Jack greet the adults and Betsy and Jenny's little voices above them, asking for her. When Becky left the room to make the tea, through the half-open door, she watched the girls laughing and dancing around their parents. As if to calm them, Boy, scooped up the youngest, pulling his wife close with his free arm. Both in profile, their heads nuzzled together, Eva closed her eyes and they kissed. Through the bannisters, unseen, Sylvia stared, fascinated.

She was acutely aware of the affection between some of her married relatives, because her aunt and uncle behaved so differently towards each other. Every time Jack put his arm around Becky or tried to show her any kind of physical affection, she would always shrug him off, telling him to 'stop acting the goat'. It upset Sylvia to see Jack rejected, when he was such a loving man. Watching how her father kissed her stepmother from the stairs, made her heart ache for Jack and for herself.

Jenny's head rested on her father's shoulders and from this position she had a clear view of Sylvia staring in through the bannisters.

"Sylvie", she screamed in delight. "Come and play with us!" Her parents broke away from each other in embarrassment as Sylvia grabbed Jenny's outstretched hand.

"Whatever are you playing at Sylvia?" said Eva, frowning at the little girl. She was a tall, lean woman and she appeared to Sylvia to be talking from a great and frosty height.

"I was just sitting on the stairs," she murmured, looking at Boy and hoping for a sign that he was pleased to see her. She beamed when he put Jenny down and turned his gaze fully towards her.

"Well, let's see 'ow tall the big girl in the family is now, shall we? Sylvia followed her father to the far wall where the year before he'd taken a pencil stub from behind his ear to record her height. Jenny followed hoping to impress with her growth too.

Eva, disinterested, busied herself with tidying Betsy's hair. She was always glad when these visits came to an end. Sylvia was a constant reminder that her husband had loved another woman before her. That she was not his first choice. Rose, and any discussion of her was a taboo subject as far as Eva was concerned and she'd told Boy that's how it had to be. She would help him to forget, to move forward with the life he deserved. Attachment to his eldest child would only hold him back. She'd given him two

165

daughters to lavish his affection on. Betsy and Jenny should be enough. When she looked at Sylvia she only saw a stranger's child. Becky and Jack's child. Not his and not theirs. Never.

The conversation between Boy and Jack turned to adult concerns. In Berlin, Adolf Hitler had recently spoken to an adoring crowd of German youth. Jack worried that it might encourage more attacks on Jewish businesses by local anti-Semites in their own neighbourhood.

"You're right. Remember the trouble in Mile End Road after Cable Street?" said Boy. When Oswald Mosley's Blackshirts were prevented from marching down Cable Street, two years earlier, fascist sympathisers took their revenge.

"The Jews are an easy target," Jack concluded. Everyone concurred with that.

Meanwhile the three little girls had slipped away unnoticed to play in the back room. Betsy was concealing something behind her back. "Sylvie, we've made something for you," she began.

"Because you only have one dolly," said Jenny.

"Be quiet, Jenny, you're spoiling the surprise," said Betsy, holding out a rag doll, crudely constructed from scraps of material. An adult hand had clearly helped with the sewing and stuffing, but the sad little object still failed to impress its new owner with its mis-matched black button eyes and oversized half-moon mouth. Strands of thin brown wool had been wrapped around its head for hair.

Sylvia stared at the object, silent. Jenny took it from her sister's outstretched hand and placed it in the empty doll's pram in the corner of the room. With great solemnity Betsy and Jenny wheeled the little pram down the hall and parked it in the bedroom.

After tea it was time to say goodbye. The adults exchanged kisses and the girls kissed Jack and Becky goodbye. Only Sylvia hung back, nervous and unsure, glancing at Becky and remembering the instructions.

Boy bent down to her. "Bye, bye big girl. See you again, soon," he said. He stayed at her level, waiting.

"Bye," she said.

"No kiss, for your father, Sylvia?" said Eva.

"She's not in a kissin' mood today," said Boy, getting to his feet, with a hurt look.

"No, I...but..."

Sylvia looked for Becky, fearful, then tearful. Whatever she did, someone seemed to say it was wrong, but Becky was already hurrying them out, oblivious to a small child's aching heart.

Sylvia took the rag doll out of the pram, sat on the bed and studied it closely. The very sight of it made her angry. She twisted and pulled at one button eye until it hung by a thread. She hated the sight of it. "If my mother had to go, why did she leave me behind," she yelled at the doll. Its hanging eye dangled on its chest. She hurled the doll across the room as hard as she could, tears of rage running down her face. Sobbing into her pillow, she wished with all her heart that that she could go to sleep and wake up as someone else.

8

When the Germans started bombing the East End you might think family tensions would be laid aside. Not by Becky. News had reached her ears that unscrupulous individuals took advantage of the nightly air raid warnings to steal from unprotected shops and homes, fuelling the suspicions she already harboured about Boy.

When the sirens went off one night, they'd all left the house in a such a hurry that the back door was left ajar. The worry had kept Becky awake all night, not that she would have slept much anyway, jammed into the shelter with so many others. The next morning, back at the house, her worst fears were confirmed.

"Ach! I knew it. Jack, come 'ere. The money's gone! He's taken it," she cried. Jack appeared at the door in his vest and his old work trousers. He'd been shaving in the scullery and had only completed half the job. "Whatever are you shouting about now, woman?" he said.

Becky was motionless by the sideboard, pointing a finger at bare wood. "The money! I left it right there. Two ten bob notes and some silver. Boy's been in an' 'elped himself. Didn't I say he was a *gonif*?"

"Don't be daft. You never leave money out like that. It must be in a drawer somewhere. And 'as for 'im coming in, with an air raid going on, and the danger of bombs falling, well... He faltered when Becky gave him one of her looks.

"Don't you bamboozle me. I know I left it right there and now it's gone. "I wouldn't put it past 'im to get 'old of an Air Raid Protection helmet and armbands so 'e could nose around empty places wiv a torch," she said. "Stealin' from 'is own, is nuffin' to 'im."

"Well, I don't think you can outright accuse..." began Jack.

"Course I can't! And especially not in front of Eva. Gawd, did you see what she 'ad on the other week? Too modern for 'er own good, that woman is. Everyone knows she 'ad her hooks in him before poor Rose was in 'er grave..." She fell silent when Jack's broad smile indicated Sylvia had come into the room, unnoticed. Sylvia knew very well that conversations that suddenly tailed off in her presence were obviously not meant for her ears, which of course made them infinitely more interesting. She'd once overheard Becky remark that Eva wasn't a patch on Rose, not nearly as sweet-natured, or pretty. She'd waited on the other side of the kitchen door, holding her breath, hoping for more, but she only heard a loud sshhhing noise and then silence. Another valuable titbit. Knowing that Becky didn't approve of Eva was comforting in a funny sort of way, but she wished it didn't have to be so secret. She slid into Jack's open arms and buried her face in his chest, where she could hear his heart beating.

"Why haven't you got your shirt on yet? You are a silly billy," she said looking up at him and they both laughed.

"What am I going to do while you're away?" he sighed, stroking her hair. Sylvia closed her eyes. With the nearby docks a strategic target for bombing, all the children in the area were

169

being sent to a safer place. The whole of Stepney Green Jewish School, including the teachers and the headmistress were being evacuated to Windsor the next morning.

"Why can't you and Auntie Becky be 'vacuated too?" she asked.

"Because evacuation is a special trip to the country just for children and the teachers," he said. "All the other grown-ups have to stay behind to protect the houses from the bombs, but it's only for a little while. You must be very brave and not be any trouble, sweetheart." He held her close, so she wouldn't see his eyes filling up.

"But who will be looking after us?" said Sylvia.

Becky and Jack exchanged glances, not knowing what to say. Letting Sylvia go in the knowledge that she would be delivered to total strangers was agony for them both. Becky only agreed to it on the strict understanding that she was not to be separated from her older cousin Milly under any circumstances. They must be housed together.

"If the family you go to 'as chickens there'll be plenty of fresh eggs to eat," said Becky, "and we'll send you food parcels as well, just as soon as we know the address," she added in a hollow tone.

The next morning Milly and Sylvia joined their classmates in a jolly march to the station. Tearful parents waved their children off, with Becky and her sister-in-law Fanny amongst them. Sylvia saw them both dabbing at their eyes and for a moment she felt like crying too, but then she remembered how Jack had told her to be brave, so like Milly she smiled and waved as if they weren't at all frightened of being separated from the adults they knew. Like most of their peers, they'd never been away from home before. With gas masks on their backs, labels round their necks,

170

and everyone they knew left behind, Sylvia, nine and Milly, thirteen, were setting off on the biggest adventure of their lives. Prior to this moment, a day trip to Southend or Margate had been the extent of their travel experience.

They arrived at Windsor Town Hall, tired and hungry, waiting to be selected by local residents, as they were told would happen. As the time passed more adults arrived but no one seemed willing to take two children together, especially girls. They were the only ones left when they saw a stout woman with a frowning face looking in their direction. The billeting officer beckoned them over. What was going to happen to them now? By this time Millie and Sylvia felt more like little orphans than adventurers.

"I'm looking for strong boys who can help my husband in the laundry," said the frowning woman in a sharp tone while the billeting officer consulted his list.

"We may be able to meet your requirements, in due course Mrs Barrow, but can you take these girls for now?" he said.

"Only on the understanding that they are replaced for boys as soon as possible. The laundry work is my priority, you must understand that." 'The laundry', as the billeting officer was only too aware, was the Royal Laundry at Windsor Castle. Mrs Barrow looked grimly at the girls and pursed her lips. "I need lads with the strength to lift and carry before they go to school. I can't be waiting hand and foot on these two useless articles," she added. Sylvia and Milly gripped each other's hands tightly. Mrs Barrow's remarks were not exactly comforting.

"Well, what are you waiting for? Christmas? Follow me," she barked at them, and with that Mrs Barrow swept out of the door, the two girls, holding tight to their little cases and gas masks, as they ran to keep up with her.

When they were shown the bedroom they would share, their spirits lifted. It was a bright and cheerful space, but relief was short lived.

"There are some rules in this house, so listen carefully," began Mrs Barrow. "Since I can't trust you to help in the laundry you will only be allowed downstairs for meals. At all other times you will remain in your room until called. Second, I won't have any truck with fussy eaters. You'll eat what you're given and be grateful for it. Do I make myself clear?" The girls nodded sadly. "Wash your hands, the pair of you and wait until I call you to the table." Mrs Barrow pointed to a basin and jug on the table and left the girls to it.

"At least we're 'ere together, Sylvie," whispered Milly. "Maybe it'll be alright, when we've got used to it." Sylvia wished that she had Milly's faith.

At the table that first evening the girls learned that the Barrows had a great fondness for rabbit which presented some problems for two Jewish children, used to a kosher diet. Rabbits belonged in fields, rather than on dinner plates, they thought. Remembering Mrs Barrow's house rules, they forced it down in silence, too hungry to care.

As Becky predicted, the Barrows kept chickens in their back garden, but no eggs were offered to the children and they were too frightened to ask for them. As the first week came to an end, they had the impression that food in general was in shorter supply than at home, but as they were never allowed downstairs when Mr Barrow, his wife and their grim-faced adult daughter were eating, it was hard to tell. Breakfast was either a little bowl of porridge with a speck of blackcurrant jam or one slice of bread with the thinnest scraping of margarine. Evening meals were mashed carrot, swede and potato or rabbit stew.

Mostly Mrs Barrow bustled about as they ate, eyeing their progress as she went about her chores. If she busied herself in the next-door pantry, the Barrow's mongrel kept watch. Digger the dog proved to be a faithful ally the next time Peter Rabbit was on the menu, though. Morsels of bunny were passed under the kitchen table to a grateful hound as soon as Mrs Barrow's attention was diverted. She had already made it clear that any food left on their plates, would be kept and presented to them the next evening. The dog's docile nature persuaded the girls to be playful and to take bigger risks when Mrs Barrow's back was turned. When Digger was caught eating from the plate that Sylvia had helpfully placed on the floor, Mrs Barrow took her revenge.

"That's what you think of the fine dinner I'm providing for you, is it? Very well, let's see if you prefer going without," she shouted into Sylvia's ear.

The next night they were called to the kitchen and were forced to stand and watch while the rest of the Barrow family tucked into a large crusty loaf, cheese and creamy butter. Sylvia and Milly's mouths watered as Mrs Barrow handed her husband and daughter dishes of juicy, sweet pears from a tin. Sylvia remembered Becky purchasing the same kind with her food coupons.

"And let that be a lesson to you both! Now help me clear away the dishes and then off to bed with you," said Mrs Barrow as her husband and daughter nodded in hostile agreement.

Before they got into bed, hungry and tearful, Sylvia and Milly tried to wash themselves as best they could from the small basin placed in their room. After two weeks with the Barrows the pair looked and felt grubby. They were beginning to regret the pact they'd made not to say anything about Mrs Barrow in the letters they sent home, or to ask about the food parcels that hadn't materialised. The adults must have enough to worry about already.

"Shall we run away?" asked Sylvia when they were both in bed.

"No. I've got a better idea," said Milly. "I thought about doing this before but now it's an emergency," she said. "Before school, we'll go back to the Town Hall and tell the billeting officer how mean Mrs Barrow is and then he'll find us somewhere else," said Milly. She squeezed Sylvia's hand under the thin blanket.

The next day they set off for school as usual, knowing they were on a secret mission. Milly remembered exactly where the Town Hall was and as they climbed the steps, it was decided that she would do the talking as she was the elder of the two. In the event, overcome by responsibility and fear, Milly lost her nerve and it was left to Sylvia to speak for them both when the kindly billeting officer beckoned them forward.

"Please sir, could we change our billet?" she managed, before bursting into tears. The billeting officer listened without interruption, as between them they stammered out the details. With matted hair and stained clothes, the neglect was plain to see so he sent them off to school, with reassurances that alternative arrangements would be made that evening. In what seemed a miracle to the children, there was a loud knock on the Barrow's door that afternoon. The billeting officer had made a call to

London and Becky and Golda had arrived to take them home. Polite introductions were hardly necessary.

"Where are they?" said Golda.

Mrs Barrow nodded grimly and led the two women upstairs.

A mixture of pride and relief burned within Sylvia at the sight of Becky standing at the door, taut and fearsome as a tiger. She pushed past Mrs Barrow and threw herself into Becky's arms. As they gathered their belongings Mrs Barrow stayed in the room, watching their every move. When it came out that the food parcels sent from London, containing the family's canned fruit and sweet rations had not been seen by the girls, the mood turned ugly.

"What? Yer tellin' me she never gave you what we sent yer?" said Golda, jerking her head towards Mrs Barrow. Now she'll get her comeuppance thought Sylvia.

"You wicked thievin' cow," screamed Becky.

"What did you call me? I don't have to take insults in my own house, from a Jew," said Mrs Barrow. In a beat, Becky's hands went for Mrs Barrow's throat. Sylvia and Milly stood by, eyes wide with terror, clutching their suitcases. Golda pulled her furious sister away just as Mr Barrow, alerted by his wife's screams appeared, red-faced at the doorway.

"What's the hell's going on here? Clear off, right now, all of you," he said, shaking a clenched fist. "That's gratitude for you. Come away, dear, you know full well that's how the Jews behave. They're all the same," he added, taking his shocked wife by the hand.

The women scooped up the girls and clattered down the stairs. On the train back it was decided that they would all take their chances in London, but by this time Hitler's bombing campaign was relentless. To escape the Blitz, the family moved to Leicester where they remained for the duration of the war. News reached them that Boy had been called up, and with Eva and the girls evacuated to another area of the country, the awkward visits and complaints from Becky stopped. For a while.

9

Leicester was not targeted by the Luftwaffe as London was, but still there was no respite from the nightly wail of sirens and the drone of enemy aircraft overhead. German fighter pilots had their sights set on destroying nearby Coventry, a major centre of war production, and Leicester was on the flightpath. Indiscriminate damage to Leicester's civilians and infrastructure was a constant threat. Soon after they arrived Jack joined the Home Guard and spent several nights a week on patrol, ready to capture any German pilot that dared to land. Clara worked in a local factory that supplied uniforms for the army and Golda assembled aircraft components. Perhaps because of her age, Becky hadn't yet been called up for war work.

Golda walked to work from their lodgings and some days she and Jack left the house at the same time. By day Jack was helping to turn waste ground into productive vegetable plots and a morning's digging got him out of the house.

On one morning he'd been on the receiving end of Becky's bad temper and had left, slamming the door behind him in frustration. Golda grabbed her coat, running to catch him up. He turned when he heard her steps, shifting the spade he was carrying from one shoulder to the other so they could talk as they walked along.

"The whole street must have 'eard her shouting the odds this morning," said Golda. "Whatever are we gonna to do wiv 'er?" she said.

"It's the war, I suppose. It's getting her down," said Jack. They carried on their way, thinking their own thoughts. Becky had bellowed at him over nothing really. Just for being in the way when she'd wanted to wash the kitchen floor. Golda tried to remember if her sister had been any different before the war. Probably not. As they walked along, the silence between them was comfortable rather than awkward.

"Do you still love Becky?" Golda asked at last. The answer didn't come immediately.

"I care for her very much," he said at last. "She's my wife after all," he said with a sigh.

"That's not what I asked," said Golda, but Jack was looking in the other direction as they crossed the road and didn't hear. She thought it strange that in all the years she'd lived under their roof she'd never seen a demonstration of love, a kiss or cuddle between them or even an anniversary card. Cooking Jack's favourite meals was as far as Becky's affection went. Funny Jack chose 'care' over 'love' to describe his relationship with her. He 'cared' for Becky because that was his nature. Now she thought about it maybe Becky was the reason they hadn't had any children of their own. She wouldn't blame Jack if he'd had a secret fancy woman in London. He would be missing her company now. Come to think of it, he used to slip out of the house in Stepney Green and be gone for hours. Where did he go? He was no drinker so he wouldn't be drowning his sorrows in a pub, she was sure of that. There were plenty of good time girls hanging around the docks. Golda

178

glanced at Jack and wondered. Ach, no, he was too good for that kind of thing.

The conversation turned to Sylvia and how she seemed to be enjoying school in Leicester. "She's got more confidence now she's made some friends," said Golda. "Becky made her frightened of her own shadow in London, with all her worrying." Jack nodded in agreement.

They'd reached the factory gate. "'Ere we are then. God bless," he said, squeezing her arm.

"See you later, and can you bring back a cabbage from the allotment? Becky's doing stuffed hearts for our dinner," she called.

"Will do." He stood at the gate, watched her clock in and waited until the factory door closed behind her. It was no use thinking what might have been. He'd married the wrong sister and that was that.

******

Back at home, after Jack had slammed the door behind him that morning, Becky stood with the bucket in her hand, unable to move. Somehow the effort of shouting at Jack had used up all the energy she had. It took all her strength just to put the bucket back in the sink. She sat down at the kitchen table and rested her head in her hands. The headaches were getting more frequent, but the doctors wouldn't listen. If she could just have a few hours of uninterrupted sleep it might help. Then she might feel more like tackling the floor. That's what she'd do while it was quiet, but Sylvia would be coming back from school for lunch soon. Perhaps she'd could leave her a note, just this once.

179

She looked in the drawer for a pencil and scrap of paper. She found a stub of pencil but nothing to write on. "Never somefink to write on when you need it," she muttered to herself, as she rummaged in the drawer. She came across a few old photos. The back of one of them would do. She looked at the image. Golda and herself smiling in the sunshine, wearing summer hats, back in Stepney Green. It seemed a lifetime ago. She turned the image over and wrote. *'In bed. Bad head. Warm up bubble and squeak in frying pan. Left custard in saucepan for you'*. She left the note on the table, propped up against the salt cellar.

Just after noon, Sylvia, let herself in from school. She was nearly thirteen. The house was quiet. She saw Becky's coat was still on the hook and read the note on the table. After she'd eaten, the bucket in the sink sparked an idea. There was just enough time to clean the floor. It would save Becky a job. She went into the adjoining scullery and placed the bucket under the drainage tap of the gas-fired 'copper' that supplied washday hot water. When a couple of inches had collected in the bucket she took it back to the sink and ran the cold tap until the temperature of the water felt comfortable to her hand.

She didn't think too much about the method. Becky was always saying that housework wore her out so this would be one job she could tick off her weekly list. She'd be so pleased. She got down on her hands and knees as she had seen Becky do and plunged a cloth into the bucket. She squeezed it out and set to work, moving it back and forth over the stone flags. It was harder than she thought. She'd only covered a fraction of the floor, but the cloth already looked ragged and the water dirty. Too late she realised that she'd failed to plan the task correctly. To empty the bucket of dirty water and fill it with fresh, she'd have to walk over the washed areas before they were dry. The sound of the bucket scraping against the sink brought Becky from her bed before Sylvia had time to address this problem.

"What the bloomin' 'ell's goin' on down there?" she shouted from the stairs.

"I'm washing the floor for you, but I haven't finished yet. Some bits are wet," she called up. "I'll tell you when it's dry, shall I?" said Sylvia, over the sound of running water but Becky was already at the doorway, inspecting the floor.

"Wet? All you've done is push the dirt around. Did you sweep first? No! Did you scrub it with a brush? No!" She bent down and rubbed her hand across the surface of the stone. "Look, at this dirt 'ere. You'll put me in an early grave, at the finish, wiv this kind of useless 'elp. If you want somefing doin', do it yerself."

Sylvia stood open mouthed, hurt in her eyes as Becky snatched the bucket from her motionless hand.

"No wonder my nerves are bad," she muttered, banging the bucket down on the floor as Sylvia ran from the room. How stupid it was to even think she could help, but she wouldn't try again. She marched back to school with hate in her heart, longing for freedom from Becky's control. When she was a grown-up, she'd have her own house. She'd be in charge and Becky wouldn't be able to do a thing about it.

******

"How do you mean, three mothers?" Alan took another drag of his cigarette. Sylvia's home life was clearly more complicated than his. It was 8 May 1945 and VE Day celebrations had broken out spontaneously across the city. Alan and Sylvia had met in the park. They'd arrived with a group of their friends but had paired off, leaving the singing and dancing behind. As they stood together on the corner of his street, getting to know each other, he couldn't help noticing that Sylvia didn't seem very relaxed. She kept looking over her shoulder every minute. Most of the time he was talking to the back of her head.

"My aunt Becky adopted me, but her two sisters live with us. Clara and Golda. One out of the three is bound to catch me doing something I shouldn't and anyway I said I'd be back by now," she said, stepping a little closer so he could kiss her.

"You could stay for a minute more and have a smoke with me," he whispered. "What's the harm?"

"You don't understand what they're like," she said. He was so good looking and the joyful mood in the park was infectious. "Oh, go on then," she said. She'd never had a cigarette before, but Alan didn't know that. She bent her head towards the lighted match and giggled as cigarette smoke billowed into the evening air above them because she didn't know you were supposed to inhale.

He slipped his arm around her waist and they kissed until she pulled away. He opened his eyes to find she was being dragged out of his grasp.

"Rosie, whatcha ya fink ya doin'?" screeched a tiny voice. A furious little woman with red cheeks and unruly hair had appeared from the alley way behind them. Sylvia froze, the cigarette dropping from her fingers, forgotten.

"You said you was goin' to the park wiv girls and 'ere you are smokin' and cavortin' in broad daylight with a boy! Yer Aunt Becky'll go bloomin' mad. She told me to foller yer' and it's a good

182

job I did," said Clara maintaining a vice-like grip on Sylvia's arm. Sylvia hung her head in embarrassment at what her new companion must be thinking.

Alan wasn't easily intimidated but decided to remain silent. He was beginning to grasp the concept of Sylvia having three mothers. Hearing her called 'Rosie' was a bit unexpected, though. Maybe she'd told him a fib about her real name or maybe this strange little woman was a bit simple.

"You're comin' right back 'ome with me," said Clara, taking Sylvia's hand and yanking her forward.

"And as fer you, young man, keep away. She's not fer the likes of you," she said. "Understand?" Alan shrugged and turned to go. Too much trouble this one. He didn't need it.

As they turned into the alley, Clara released her grasp.

"Rose, this ain't fair on Becky. You'll make 'er sick if you carry on like this. Make us all sick," she said, her voice wavering.

Sylvia said nothing. Clara's comments only rubbed it in. They were all old people, out of touch. They would never understand how much she longed to be out of their control. Alan wasn't Jewish. That was at the bottom of it. Telling lies to meet a *yok* would make it an even worse sin in Becky's eyes. She feared what Clara would tell Becky, but she would have to face it. Disappointing Jack was what really troubled her. She couldn't bear to see the hurt on his face again, like that time she'd gone carol singing with her school friends.

It hadn't even occurred to her that Christmas carols were about celebrating the birth of Jesus but offending his religious principles must have felt like a rejection of *him*. She just liked the tunes and being the same as everyone else for once. It was all

Becky's fault for making her stand out like a sore thumb in Leicester, first by telling everyone about the adoption and then by putting the kibosh on swimming lessons. She was the only girl in her class who couldn't swim. Swimming, according to Becky was yet another dangerous thing that was fine for everyone else to do, but not Sylvia.

"Sorry," said Sylvia to the ground when she and Clara arrived back home, and the details were reported back. Becky was already waiting outside the house, wringing her hands in despair.

"You'll be the death of me," Becky complained. "After all we've done fer you, an' all," she said, shaking her head. "A *yok* she wants. This is what we get. Outta my sight."

Sylvia went in and found Jack sitting in the kitchen. She sat down at the table, without meeting his eyes, until Jack pushed a cup of tea towards her.

"She'll get over it," he said in a weary tone. He put his cup in the sink and laid a reassuring hand on her shoulder. It was alright. He was on her side. He turned on the wireless and they both listened to the broadcaster repeating the joyous news of Germany's surrender and the end of war in Europe. From their kitchen, Sylvia and Jack smiled and cheered. Just two weeks before, they had been silenced by the reporter's account of Bergen-Belsen concentration camp. Piles of decaying corpses, the pleas for water from those barely hanging on to life. A hellhole of misery, one of many devised and created by a murderous regime. Sylvia had put her hands over her ears, begging Jack to switch it off.

Now there was talk of returning to London, but they wouldn't be going back to Copley Street. Bombs had left deep wide craters on the streets they knew and many of the houses were ruins.

"We'll miss Leicester, won't we Sylv?

"Going back will be like starting all over again," she said. There was a lost look in her eyes that he hadn't seen since she was a child. In two days, she'd turn fifteen. His little girl was growing up.

10

By the close of 1945 the family had moved back to London and were living at 48, Norcott Road, Stoke Newington, a rented terraced house that would be home for many years, but the household had changed. Golda had married and set up home with her husband in Leytonstone. For a while everyone felt a little unsettled by her absence.

Sylvia longed for the friends of her own age that she'd made in Leicester. They'd made promises to keep in touch, but it already seemed that the letters were coming less often. Perhaps a train trip to see them wouldn't be out of the question.

"You can get that idea right outta ya 'ead, my girl," said Becky, over her shoulder, from the sink. "Trains, to Leicester she wants now!" "Escaped the bombs and now she wants to go worryin' me half to death wiv gallivantin' on trains, 'alfway round the country," she added, slapping a dishcloth on the draining board for emphasis. Any further discussion on a forbidden rail journey was pointless, unless she wanted to be blamed for a severe decline in Becky's health.

One of Sylvia's friends in Leicester had an older sister who was a hairdresser. In the school holidays, during the war, they'd sometimes swept up the cuttings and rinsed the brushes and combs. At the end of the day, some silver would be slipped in their pockets, so they felt like proper workers. Sylvia had saved the money. It wasn't a lot, but it was hers to spend as she liked and that felt good. She quite fancied being a hairdresser but predictably, this idea was soon quashed. Now they were back in London, Becky decreed that Sylvia should train to be a secretary. A family connection to a firm of solicitors was explored for opportunities but the senior partner advised Becky that it would be unethical for Sylvia to work for him. Instead, he would speak to a good friend in another legal firm who might be able to help. An appointment was duly arranged at Freeman and Company in Holborn.

When Morris Freeman beckoned the elderly woman and her silent young companion into his office, his first thoughts for the girl were pity. She had such a sorrowful expression on her face when he shook her hand. Poor thing.

"You'll take 'er on 'an she'll learn shorthand and typing at Pitmans, then?" said Becky as if she was the decision-maker, rather than the learned man behind the desk. Sylvia squirmed at Becky's *chutzpah*. Mr Freeman wasn't being given much choice.

After she started work Sylvia thought Morris Freeman must have kept her on to avoid another encounter with Becky. At fifteen she made appalling spelling errors and knew next to nothing about office work, but gradually, as she grew in confidence, her work began to improve. He let her leave early on the days she studied shorthand and typing at Pitmans College, and although she hated the lessons, she managed to learn what was necessary, devising her own version of shorthand along the way. Much later Morris told her that when he saw her with Becky he thought there was a great sadness about her that he wanted to see disappear.

It was about a year later that a letter addressed to Sylvia, in Eva's handwriting arrived at home. She'd got their address from other relatives and thought Sylvia should know they had returned to London and were living just a short bus ride away. There was an invitation to visit the following Saturday, when Betsy and Jenny would be at home and her father, still a bookmaker, would join them when he could.

Sylvia could hardly believe that after all this time, her father wanted to see her. The letter didn't exactly say that, but that's what she wanted to believe. She was curious to see where they all lived and best of all, the invitation was for her and her alone. There was no mention of Becky. At least Eva recognised that she was old enough not to need a chaperone.

"You don' 'ave to go, yer know," said Becky. "Trust 'er to make the first move. God forbid your father, should invite you 'isself." Whoever made the invitation, would have been in the wrong in Becky's eyes but for once Sylvia could decide. She was going and Becky would just have to live with it.

******

When the day came, Sylvia took great care with her appearance, brushing her shoulder length bobbed hair till it shone. She put on a navy tea dress with white buttons and noted with some satisfaction how the belt emphasised her tiny waist. Now to find the right shoes. She tried on a pair of black court shoes but no, they looked too heavy. As it wasn't raining, she settled on a pair of black suede, peep toe shoes with little heels.

She left the house with Becky's instructions ringing in her ears to be careful and be back before it got dark.

The bus made its way, past the war-damaged streets where kids played in the debris and women in aprons swept their front steps. It slowed to a halt to let a line of men snake their way across the road to a football match. Sylvia took her powder compact from her bag, checked her face in the mirror, and stepped off at the next stop. Crossing the road, she headed for the London County Council's brick-built blocks, offering tenants modern, convenient living.

The flat was on the fourth floor at the end of a draughty exterior walkway. She knocked on the door. Would she recognise them all and they her? The door opened to reveal Eva's familiar haughty, half smile. In a second Eva's eyes noted every detail of Sylvia's appearance. "Lovely to see you, Sylvia, come in," she said at last. "The girls and your father will be in shortly." Sylvia followed Eva down a small hallway to the kitchen. The flat smelt homely, comfortable, not musty and old like the house at Norcott Road. No matter how hard they all scrubbed and cleaned, the house was so decrepit, it hardly made a difference. Here everything looked polished and new, from the neat little gas stove in the corner to the painted kitchen cupboards. She wondered what was making the background whirring noise in the kitchen. It sounded like an engine ticking over. She sat at the table, taking it all in as Eva filled the kettle.

"We have a lovely home here, don't you think?" she said.

Sylvia heard the words, but they didn't register. Eva had taken a bottle of milk from the refrigerator and the whirring noise had stopped when she'd opened the door. They only had a wobbly old meat safe in the scullery at home.

"Yes, it's a proper refrigerator, I can tell you're wondering," said Eva. "Your father bought it for me the other week. It's the latest model."

Sylvia smiled knowingly and made all the right noises. She didn't feel envious. It was like looking through a window at a stranger's home. She didn't belong and she knew she never would.

"We'll have a sandwich when everyone's home," said Eva, handing Sylvia a cup of tea. As she busied herself with bread, mustard and salt beef, Eva hummed a little tune to herself. She looked the epitome of a fashionable 1940s housewife with her dark hair, swept up in a tight roll, and wide high waisted trousers. If things had been different they might have been friends. Eva was only in her thirties after all and closer to Sylvia's age than any of her relatives.

Just then they heard the key in the door and the girls' voices shouting, "Hello, we're back."

Betsy and Jenny tumbled into the kitchen and they all embraced in a flurry of recognition and laughter. "Look at you two, taller than me now!" said Sylvia. "I have to put my heels on to get a bit of height."

Boy appeared at the doorway, looking awkward and unsure. He glanced at Eva, casually standing by the sink, with her arms folded.

"Come in and say hello to Sylvia, then," she said as if she wanted him to get it over with.

"Hello Dad," said Sylvia. He gave her an awkward kiss on the cheek. The look in his eyes told her, that he would have liked to throw both his arms around her and hug her tight, but in Eva's presence he was holding back. The sandwiches were passed around and the conversation turned to Sylvia's job with a legal firm and Betsy's apprenticeship to a seamstress. There were enquiries about other members of the family and some inconsequential pleasantries exchanged until Sylvia said she should be going.

Boy took her to the door, quietly handing her a five-pound note. He put his finger to his lips. "Don't mention this to Eva," he mouthed. He slipped the money in her pocket, when she declined to take it. She left without a word. His weakness revolted her.

On the way home she played the events of the afternoon back in her mind, marvelling at Eva's cleverness in making her feel superficially welcome for her own amusement, but it had backfired. She wouldn't just disappear because another woman felt threatened by her. She smiled to herself at her response. She wouldn't be hurt, and she wouldn't let herself be crushed. Eva seemed to have turned her father into a responsible and respectable citizen, but she had also cast herself as the wicked stepmother. Maybe she'd had a lucky escape. If Eva had brought her up, she would have been little more than a servant in her father's household.

Back at home, for once Sylvia took pleasure in sharing every detail with Becky who, interjected, exclaimed, tutted and disapproved to her heart's content.

******

Work gave Sylvia a degree of independence, but she longed for more and especially a social life with friends of her own age.

Every day, on the bus to work she saw young office girls, just like herself. Overhearing conversations about their weekends only made her feel lonelier. The most she did was go to the pictures with her aunts or cousins. Jack had taken a job as a cinema usher and he would sometimes show them to their seats, his torch lighting their way to the correct row. When the film started, he'd watch from the back. They could always find out from Jack what was showing next and who the stars were. Clark Cable, Bette Davis and Elizabeth Taylor were her favourites. If it was a musical like *The Jolson Story* or one starring Judy Garland they'd all come back humming the tunes.

One rainy morning, she got on the bus as usual. It was crowded and damp and she was too busy grappling with a dripping wet umbrella to pay much attention to the passenger already in the seat next to her, until the conductor arrived with his ticket machine. She had her money ready and took the ticket. The girl beside her was still trying to find her purse. "I must have left it at home," she said, after scrabbling in her bag and both coat pockets, "unless it's fallen on the floor." Sylvia and the girl looked under the seat in the little space allowed.

"I can't see anything, down there," said Sylvia, "Look, don't worry, I've got enough change, let me get your ticket." She handed the conductor the money. The girl didn't look the sort to pull a fast one and it was filthy weather to get off and walk.

"Oh, how kind of you. Thank you so much. You've really got me out of a fix," she said, taking the ticket. "I'm Lillian, by the way."

"I'm Sylvia. I get off at the next stop."

"I must pay you back. I always get this bus. I'll look for you, tomorrow. Cheerio, and thanks again," she said. They waved their goodbyes as the bus moved off.

As the weeks went by they looked out for each other every day. Lillian, Sylvia learned, was nineteen and lived with her mother. Her father had died in the war. She worked in a bank, but she wasn't too keen on her job. The manager of the bank was a bit too full of himself for one thing and made suggestive comments to all the women in the bank, despite being married.

"Mr Freeman is very proper and there never any hint of that sort of thing," said Sylvia. "But then again he met my Aunt Becky and that would be enough to scare any man into behaving."

Lillian was keen to meet Mr Right and was full of stories about the popular dinner dance venues in the West End that she'd been to with that quest in mind. Maybe they could go to one together? "The one at Murray's Club, near Regent Street is the best," said Lilian. "It's so glamorous, you'd love it."

Sylvia listened, wide-eyed as Lilian painted a picture of a vast hall with chandeliers where a dance band performed for well-heeled clientele. Upstairs, a semi-circular dining area overlooked the dance floor and stage, with access via an enormous curved staircase. More tables and chairs for couples and groups were arranged on three sides of the dance floor, behind enormous pillars. Waiters in white jackets and bow ties glided discreetly between the tables whilst cabaret singers and dancers entertained the guests. After dinner was served, there was dancing, to music provided by live musicians till at least 11pm. It all sounded like the setting for an MGM film to Sylvia. There was just one problem.

"My aunt and uncle are quite old-fashioned, and my aunt is so strict about where I can go," said Sylvia. Lilian took this information in her stride. She'd been to Murray's Club with another friend, but that girl had met someone, and Lillian didn't fancy going by herself and looking like a wallflower. Sylvia was her route back to socialising and she wasn't about to give up on the idea that easily. Besides Sylvia knew how to dress. Lillian had felt a bit out of her league last time she'd gone to Murray's. The well to do women there wore such fabulous evening wear. Sylvia was bound to know places in the East End where you could find an affordable cocktail dress. She always looked so well turned out and it wasn't easy to get nice things. She could learn a thing or two from Sylvia about putting an outfit together and maybe then she'd stand a better chance of finding a suitable man.

"Maybe it would help if I met your aunt and uncle?" said Lillian.

"I was thinking the same thing," said Sylvia, laughing.

Lilian was duly invited home for tea, and Sylvia kept her fingers crossed. Fortunately, Becky was in an amiable mood and rather liked the fact that Lilian was a little older. Older, meant wiser and Lilian seemed a sensible girl. Permission, on this occasion was granted, though Sylvia was sure that Becky would pace the floor with worry until she heard the key in the door.

11

Leslie, the Sous Chef at the Russell Hotel had settled right back into the job he'd had before the war. Luckily, the hotel hadn't taken a direct hit during the Blitz, but the windows were blown out one night when a Doodlebug hit the nearby square. Working most weekends meant he didn't have the worry of going out and speaking to girls because he was a reserved, shy kind of man. He had one Saturday night off a month and his mother was always nagging him to go to a dance in the hope he would meet someone. He was nearly twenty-seven after all. Maybe he'd risk a night at Murray's Club. He knew a few people in the kitchen there so at least the dinner would be good. He could always take a newspaper with him and if he didn't feel brave enough to ask anyone for a dance he could sit and read it, so no one would know he was lonely.

While he was eating he saw two girls being shown to a table close to the dance floor. They didn't appear to have male companions. The dark-haired one looked a little unsure of herself and was looking around as if she couldn't quite believe where she was. He saw her take out a little mirror from her bag and check her hair was in place. He liked that. If she was unsure of herself then maybe he stood a better chance. Her companion seemed more confident and was probably harder to impress. He preferred the look of the petite girl with the mirror to her taller friend, anyway.

He called the waiter over and asked him to let the girls know that he would like to buy them a drink. He'd seen someone do that in a film. Who was it? Cary Grant or maybe Humphrey Bogart? Oh, he was hopeless with names. Never mind. It looked like the waiter had delivered his message because they were looking across and smiling. When they'd had their drinks, the waiter said they'd like him to join them. He left his newspaper on the table.

Leslie had two left feet on the dance floor but Sylvia, laughed it off and somehow they managed a semblance of a waltz. When they returned to their table, Lillian had been asked to dance, so Leslie took his opportunity.

"Perhaps we could see each other again?" "Would you fancy coming to the opera with me?" he said.

"What on earth would I wear to the opera?" she said. He just laughed and said he was sure she would look lovely in anything she chose. She enjoyed the compliment, but she secretly worried that Becky might not let her go. She'd have to take Leslie home first, but he was nearly ten years older than herself. Becky was sure to object on those grounds alone, and what would Leslie think about her circumstances? His background was so different. She felt ashamed of her own.

Leslie came from a family of bakers, skilled pâtissiers, who ran their own businesses in Camden Town and Shepherd's Bush. As young children he and his three siblings were looked after by a nanny and the family enjoyed a comfortable upbringing until 1929 when a good deal of their wealth disappeared in the Wall Street Crash. His sister had recently married an airman and had gone to live in New Zealand, but his two brothers were both still single. Like Sylvia there was a family tragedy to come to terms with too.

"Before the war, on Coronation Day actually, my father had given everyone the day off, including the bakers that made the bread through the night," he told her. "He didn't want to close the shop because we needed the money, so he lifted the two hundred-and-forty-pound sacks of flour on his back and made all the bread himself. When he came home in the morning he shouted for me to get the doctor because he had a terrible pain in his chest. I ran as fast as I could, and the doctor said he would come but by the time he arrived my father had died," he said.

"It's so vivid in my mind still, and the terrible journey to the cemetery. I was seventeen and I sobbed all the way there," he admitted. Sylvia laid a comforting arm on his.

"How terrible. What a shock," she said, shaking her head in sympathy.

"My mother carried on running the bakery and the shop in Camden Town until our street was bombed in the Blitz," he said.

"I just wish my father could have lived to see that I made a success of my chef's training. He never knew that I worked at the Ritz in Paris after catering school. This was 1938 and of course I had to come home because of the danger of war breaking out."

"I envy you because you have memories of your father to hold on to," said Sylvia. "My mother is like a flickering shadow, always just out of reach." Leslie looked in her eyes and saw anger as well as sadness.

At the end of the night he insisted on seeing the girls back on the bus. Leslie and Sylvia got off first and lingered on the corner of Norcott Road, neither wanting to say goodnight.

"It's late, you'll miss your bus back," she said, looking up the street. He knew he ought to be going. Camden Town wasn't around the corner and it was already 11pm.

Any minute now and Becky would be hurrying up the street to find her. She'd never hear the last of it if she was later than they'd agreed, and it would be dreadful if this was Leslie's introduction to her home life. She gave him a peck on the cheek and walked briskly away before her worst fears materialised.

******

"Let her go," said Jack, banging the table. Sylvia had never heard him laying down the law in quite that way before. Even Becky was shocked into silence for once.

It was a week after she'd met Leslie at Murray's Club.

It sounded so grand, 'the opera', and romantic too, thought Jack. He was a music hall man himself, but he'd fight for his girl to be at the opera. Becky scoffed.

"Opera, shmopra! Don't drive me mad. Opera, she wants now! Over my dead body."

It was different after Leslie was introduced. Even Becky could see he was gentle and sincere, and his more affluent Jewish background certainly impressed her.

"'ard to believe 'is age. Must be 'is lovely fair skin makes 'im look so young," she remarked to Sylvia. For his part Leslie only saw two genuine, decent people. Becky, he conceded might be a little intimidating to some, but she treated him with kindness and respect. To Jack, Leslie was a son from the first meeting. The differences in their backgrounds and means melted away as soon as they talked about their war service.

"I was in the Middle East," said Leslie. "Once we set up a base hospital, I joined an ambulance unit in the Western Desert.

"Ow, didja manage in the heat, Les?" said Jack.

"You get used to it. I had to wear a sun hat to begin with and then a tin hat. I was caught by a piece of shrapnel in the end and was sent back to the military hospital," said Leslie blushing. "When I was recovering they found out I could cook, and they put me in the hospital kitchens. In the Western Desert there were thousands of patients to cook for, with so many wounded coming in," he said. "Sylvia said you were a cook in France during the Great War?"

"That's right. Wasn't over for us over there till 1919, when the squadron returned 'ome," said Jack, remembering how the months seemed like years, back then.

Sylvia wasn't received quite so generously by Leslie's relatives but perhaps the fault lay with her. They were professionals, running a family firm, but to her they were akin to a royal court, with Leslie's mother presiding over them all like a matriarchal queen. The protective layer of reverse snobbery she wore in their company made her seem brittle and distant, but she was only seventeen after all. Far too young to marry, they said, so it was agreed that the couple should have a two-year engagement. Sylvia wondered how Becky and Jack would ever have enough money to pay for the sort of wedding these people would expect for their son. Somehow, with post-war shortages affecting everyone, it happened without anyone taking umbrage.

On 29th May,1949, sixty guests were invited to the La Bohème restaurant and ballroom in London's West End to celebrate the marriage of Leslie, a hotel chef, aged twenty-nine and Sylvia, a typist, aged nineteen. On the bride's side Boy, Eva, Betsy and Jenny were among the guests. Sylvia also invited her friend Lillian, and her boss, Morris Freeman. The kindly solicitor, still single, was delighted to attend and gave the couple a wedding gift of twenty-one guineas and two silver dishes. Her father gave them twenty-five pounds. The bride wore white satin and all the guests were served fresh cream gateaux for dessert, an extravagant luxury at the time. These were supplied by the groom's uncles and were kept hidden under the top table, prompting murmurs of admiration around the room when they were brought out.

They'd planned to spend their honeymoon in Paris but with money so tight the whole idea felt much too extravagant. Instead they saved all the money they'd been given as wedding presents and honeymooned in Eastbourne. They made a pact to pretend they'd been to Paris to avoid disappointing their relatives. The numerous black and white photos they took, in which the Eiffel Tower is noticeably absent from view, are of each other as separate people. She posed for him and then he passed the camera to her to capture his image.

To begin with they lived in the upstairs rooms of Becky and Jack's house. At Sylvia's insistence their first major purchase was a refrigerator and the whole house vibrated with the noise it made. As soon as money allowed, they moved out to a small house in Northolt, prompting Becky to take to her bed in protest, until Leslie said he'd come over to collect them in his car whenever they wanted to visit.

After an interval, a healthy daughter was born with a warning that future pregnancies required careful monitoring, and a hospital delivery. A home birth should never be considered.

Becky and Jack adored their little granddaughter. They bought her a toy dog on wheels with a handle at its rear, designed to encourage reluctant toddlers to walk.

12

I put away the photos of little me in the garden of the Northolt house with my toy dog on wheels. Two years after those shots were captured, my parents, Leslie and Sylvia, started to move up in the world. By then Dad had risen to Head Chef so they could afford a bigger house in a better area. They chose one in Abbotshall Avenue, Southgate and our brief time there became the stuff of family legend. A mere mention of the address was enough to make Mum grimace. I once asked Dad if he thought the house was haunted. Mum had always insisted it was.

"The people who bought the house from us, put it up for sale six months later," he said. "That was peculiar."

******

It was just the sort of home Sylvia had in mind. Three bedrooms in an 'avenue', not a street or a road. A proper, *shprauncy* avenue. They'd looked round the house in the summertime when the windows were open, and sunshine seemed to illuminate every corner.

"Lovely view of the garden," Leslie noted from the kitchen window, admiring the freshly mown lawn, apple trees and climbing roses in full bloom. Sylvia had already made up her mind. This was the one. The kitchen was such a good size. Plenty of room for a table and chairs.

"This time, next year we could be sitting here enjoying all this, as our own," she said. "It's a house we could stay in." She looked at him with a smile.

Another baby. Maybe it was time they tried.

By the time they moved in, it was late autumn, windy and wet. The rooms, previously bathed in bright light, now had shadowy corners and a gloom hung over the downstairs hall and upstairs landing. The neighbours were pleasant enough but a bit standoffish, not like they'd been in Northolt, where they saw a tiny baby grow into a little person.

******

If I close my eyes I can still picture the dark wood front door and three steps up to it, giving the impression that this house was higher than the others on the street. I had vivid, terrifying nightmares in that house. I must have started school soon after we arrived because I remember wearing a uniform and being thrust into a room full of children. I stayed helpless and silent at the edge of it all, whilst they busied themselves around me. The noise and apparent chaos made me uncomfortable. I could hardly focus. My recollection is that the room was sloping but it was more likely that I suddenly felt dizzy, lost my balance and therefore my view was skewed. The nightmares must have been tiring me out.

Mum always dismissed this version of events when it came up because in all our joint memories, her feelings were always more important than mine. I was just a child and children are always fussing about something. Besides, I was very clingy. As a young child I was fearful of my peers, refusing to join in with their games and always wanting to stay close to my mum. It used to drive her mad that I would never just go off and play with other children, but would just sit, unhappily with her, when she would have liked five minutes' peace without me.

I don't remember the recurring tonsillitis and earache that apparently made me listless and fretful. Only the nightmares. When I think about it now, these were not like frightening scenarios that very occasionally play out in my head in the early hours. The sort that wake me up, clammy and breathless, with the memory of it still beating in my chest. No, this was a nightly terror, prowling and roaring around my bed, preventing me from closing my eyes. 'They', being two male lions that paced with dripping jaws, shaking their golden manes at me. They were waiting, ready to pounce the second I nodded off. I heard them roar, looked into their cruel eyes and smelt their foul hunger. They were there and as real to me as every other object in the room. Those lions were the reason for the nightly screaming that brought Dad running in, his white pants glowing in the dark just as the lions retreated into the walls. It was always Dad that came or perhaps I demanded that he did.

The big cats turned up so regularly that an elaborate bedtime ritual was established to keep them at bay. It started with Mum reading me large chunks from one of my Milly Molly Mandy books. There was a lot of deliberate repetition of names in those stories and Mum used to say reading them aloud drove her doolally. After she told me she'd read enough Milly Molly Mandy for one night, I insisted that she pile all my books around my bed for protection. Books were magical things and it was best they were there. Dad was never in for my bedtime. I had a kind of ache in my tummy that never completely went away if Dad wasn't in the house.

******

Leslie worked long hours and with a sickly child on her hands, Sylvia was isolated. She could have coped with that but there was something about being stuck in *this* house all day that made her feel uncomfortable. In every room her steps seemed to echo in the silence and a sudden creak from the stairs made her jump out of her skin. She told herself not to be silly. It was just a case of getting used to the new surroundings. The trouble was the new surroundings appeared to be conspiring against her. For one thing the glass doors to the lounge drove her to distraction. The glass showed every mark. A magnet for dust. What a dreadful choice by the previous owners. You just don't notice these things until you live in a place, she thought, unaware that hours were passing as she polished the same area again and again.

It was the kitchen that upset her the most. The cupboards had been emptied and scrubbed several times. Yet still a crawling insect would appear from behind a tin, or be discovered, lifeless beneath a packet. One time, a large spider had crawled out from the small bag of flour she was holding. She screamed, throwing the open bag to the floor, the action coating every surface in the room in fine white powder. The spider had scuttled to who-knows-where and the noise woke her sleeping daughter. It was time she had her medicine anyway but there was no Milly Molly

Mandy that night with such a mess to sort out downstairs. When Leslie came back he found Sylvia red-eyed and anxious.

"There's something not right about this house. I think we should move," she said when he'd asked her what was wrong. He looked at her, confused at first, smiling at the suggestion.

"I'm not joking Leslie. I mean it," she said, with a sharpness in her tone that he hadn't heard before. Later that night she made him open all the cupboards to check there were no insects waiting to further aggravate her nerves.

"I don't know what you're talking about. Sparkling clean," he said, shutting the door. Leslie wasn't here in the daytime like she was. He couldn't possibly understand how claustrophobic it was, being stuck here all day with a sick child.

She felt nauseous the next morning when she heard him drive away. She'd have to go out. She didn't know where to exactly, but she couldn't stay in the house. The hairdresser. That's where she could go. It would take up the morning. Just a pity that the little one had another throat infection and a hacking cough. If it wasn't her throat, it was her ears. She hadn't had more than a week of good health since they'd moved in. Bad dreams too. It must have been the fever that brought on the night terrors. Now she'd only go to sleep in her own room if they piled books around her bed.

She bundled her daughter up in several layers, closed the door behind them and started walking in the direction of the shops. There was a biting wind and she had to drag the child along. She was glad to get them both inside. She'd just got settled in the chair when the crying started. The woman who washed hair left Sylvia and clucked round the little girl who was sitting awkwardly on a seat underneath one of the big hairdryers.

"Poor little thing aren't you feeling very well?" she said. "Ooh, she does look quite pale, doesn't she?

"Never mind about her, it's me that's worn out," said Sylvia. "I've got her linctus in my bag here", said Sylvia as a towel was placed around her wet hair. Some orange squash was found for the child, to help take away the nasty taste of the medicine.

"Come here and have it," said Sylvia, wiping the plastic spoon on her hanky. The child slid off the seat but as she took a step forward, her legs buckled under her.

Sylvia was frantic until the smelling salts brought the child round. A taxi was called to take them both home.

"I hope she's feeling better soon," said the salon receptionist to Sylvia. "Perhaps it was the smell of the hair lacquer that made her faint. I've known that to happen, when people aren't used to it, but such a shame we couldn't dry off your hair first."

******

Sylvia couldn't face eating anything that evening and was too anxious to read bedtime stories. Milly Molly Mandy was driving her bloody mad. She couldn't amuse a sick child for hours on end. She didn't have the patience for it.

"Where's Daddy? I want to wait up for Daddy."

"Just go to sleep. You're not well. Daddy's not here. Daddy's at work. Stop crying or you'll make *me* ill at the finish," she shouted, duster in hand at the bedroom door.

She went back downstairs. She'd put the oven on. Leslie might want something warming through when he got in. She was always thinking of him but what thought or attention did she get in return? She stepped into the kitchen and immediately forgot why she was there. The sink unit. Solid, fixed, immovable, yet it had somehow released itself from its fixings and was positioned at an angle to the wall. Sylvia stared in disbelief at an opening, two inches wide. With her heart banging against her chest she bent down to the floor to examine the gap. She stared at the material adhering to her fingers. It was soil.

Leslie would have preferred to stay a little longer, but the house went on the market the next week. The first couple that came to view said they loved it, especially the glass double doors, separating the lounge from the dining room. So stylish. Sylvia smiled with pride. It looked like the hours spent polishing was about to pay off with a quick sale. They had to have it, they said. It was perfect, just the sort of house they'd been looking for, they gushed.

Abbotshall Avenue was behind them. Leslie and Sylvia took their demons to a more modest home in a different part of north London. And that's when, out of the blue, Boy got in touch. Sylvia couldn't believe it when she heard his voice on the phone. It had been months since they'd last seen each other at a family wedding.

"Dad, what a lovely surprise! How are you?" she waved a free hand in Leslie's direction, silently mouthing that the caller was her father. Leslie raised a questioning eyebrow. He couldn't begin to guess how the conversation was proceeding from Sylvia's responses as the caller seemed to be doing all the talking.

"Well?" said Leslie when Sylvia finally replaced the receiver.

"He said that he's got a fantastic business opportunity we might be interested in, and he wants to come over and tell us the details," she said with a grin.

RUTH BADLEY

"Sounds very intriguing and I suppose there's no harm in hearing what he has to say," said Leslie. Two weeks later, Boy was sitting at their blue Formica kitchen table, explaining that the grocery and delicatessen shop he now managed was up for sale.

"I'm telling you, it's a little goldmine," he said with authority.

"I'm not sure," said Leslie. "I can't see myself standing behind a counter all day. I'm used to the kitchen."

"You wouldn't have to be there, Les! That's the beauty of it. You could carry on with your job and I'd manage it all. I know 'ow it all runs. You could just sit back, sign the orders and enjoy the profits. Why don't you talk it over between you and I'll let the owner know you're interested?"

"I promise we'll give it serious thought, Dad," said Sylvia at the door. She threw her arms round him in a burst of gratitude and he kissed her cheek. As Sylvia saw it, her father was trying to help her. Better late than never. Besides, she quite fancied the idea of being married to a business owner.

They'd already made up their minds to buy the shop when Sylvia, emboldened by their decision, told Becky and Jack.

"We've looked at the books and it's certainly profitable," said Leslie when he saw their worried faces.

"You must be bloomin' mad! I wouldn't touch it wiv' a barge pole," said Becky shaking her head in despair. Even Jack thought it was a risky proposition.

They went ahead nevertheless, and all was well for the first six months of trading. Leslie had gone into corporate catering by this time and could only spend Saturdays in the shop. When Boy introduced his son-in-law to the regular customers, they murmured with delight that their little neighbourhood shop had turned into a proper family business.

It lasted for longer than it should have. When Leslie did the accounts, it was clear the shop was taking money, but he wasn't at all sure it was *making* money. Baffling really. He was an innocent when it came to business and he kept thinking the situation would change. One Saturday, a regular customer quietly took Leslie to one side while Boy was supervising a delivery. She appeared nervous and reluctant to speak and kept biting her lip.

"What's the matter, Mrs Hellman? Are you unwell?" said Leslie.

"I hope I'm not speaking out of turn," she said. "Please forgive me if I am, but in my opinion you want to keep an eye on your father-in-law. There, I've said it now." She looked over her shoulder, anxious that her voice was too loud.

"Go on," said Leslie.

"I've seen him putting cash from the till in his pocket on more than one occasion," she whispered. "Did you know that when his wife and daughters come in, he tells them to help themselves from the shelves? I feel terrible telling you this, but I think you should know what I've seen," she said.

Leslie listened, grateful that someone had the courage to tell him. Most people wouldn't want to get involved.

The business was being destroyed from within and when Sylvia and Leslie confronted Boy, denials and recriminations followed. In the end Leslie's two brothers had to physically throw him off the premises. A Pakistani family bought the shop, but clearing the debts set Sylvia and Leslie back years.

Sylvia never saw or spoke to her father again.

PART THREE

1

North London, 1970s

After Mum left us, Dad and I both went a little bit crazy. He threw himself into the quest to find a replacement woman with reckless enthusiasm, and I spent far too much time worrying about how to look after the house. Euphoria at the sense of freedom from Mum's tyranny was short lived for me. Seeing how quickly the dust accumulated on previously pristine surfaces made me more anxious than I cared to admit. Dad didn't seem to notice my anxiety or the dust. We were both keeping up a pretence that meant we didn't talk about the new reality. We didn't talk much about anything, and especially not our feelings. Dad seemed distant and preoccupied with a blonde called Shirley. The pedestal I'd put him on was starting to wobble.

I'd assumed the role of housekeeper to his chef de patron without question. I couldn't think about Mum without feeling angry and resentful that we were in this situation. She'd set the standard on how the house was kept and, as I saw it, she'd dumped this onerous responsibility onto me. Far from shrugging it off, the demons in my head were telling me I had to step up, if only to prove to myself that we could get on fine without her. I suppose a psychiatrist might have said I was trying to put my life in order, to somehow mend what had been broken. With Mum taking her preoccupations to another place, you'd think I would be revelling in more independence, but instead I was on a mission to restore the status quo at home. There was a gaping hole in our house that we didn't talk about and nothing I could do would fill it. It wasn't as if she'd died but in our own ways we were both grieving. She was my mother. She was still in contact but she'd left. I hated her but I loved her too. Dad was lonely. He needed someone else and to me it seemed anyone would do.

If I'd moved to a new environment too, it might have been different. All my college friends were fending for themselves, having fun in student flats where household duties were low priority. I envied them, but there was no good reason for Dad to pay for rented accommodation when college was only a short Tube ride away from home. Except, it didn't feel like home anymore. It was my tormentor.

Every unpolished surface was evidence of my shortcomings. Even as I wiped the dust away, I saw new particles drifting down to take their place and so it started. A list of tasks that had to be completed and repeated before I could get out of the door and into some semblance of normal life. Sunny days were my enemy, with bright light illuminating the areas I'd missed. At the height of my misery I even made an unsatisfactory attempt at washing down the accessible exterior walls, plunging an old sponge into soapy water again and again until my hands were raw. The parts I couldn't reach gave me sleepless nights.

Dad mostly left the house early so remained unaware of my habits. A student timetable was my ally. As I didn't have to be at drama school until mid-morning, I had time to clean. Only once did my compulsive behaviour threaten to betray me. I arrived late

214

to a scheduled rehearsal, muttering something about the unreliable train service. In truth, I'd left the house without checking that the shoes in my wardrobe were arranged in straight lines and felt compelled to turn back as soon as I reached the station.

Some of the shoes were Mum's. She'd left them, together with a few smart dresses she didn't want. She thought they would fit. Might be useful. Especially at the weekends, when I spent time at Jeffrey's house. Apparently my boyfriend's mother looked forward to seeing another female around. With a miserable, overbearing husband and three sons, the poor woman was seriously outnumbered. She always looked exhausted and the cleaners and gardeners they employed didn't seem to alleviate her suffering at all. Every few months she would take herself off for a week of rest and relaxation, to what was referred to back then as a health farm. Having the means to escape from her family once in a while seemed to be her only pleasure.

It was an education just seeing the labour-saving gadgets they took for granted. I didn't know a machine for washing dishes even existed until I saw it in action in their kitchen. We didn't even have a machine to wash clothes at home.

I thought wearing Mum's outfits in front of them might somehow boost my status in their eyes. You could tell they were expensive. More importantly, they could tell, so I wore them at the weekend, in front of Jeffrey's family, like a protective outer layer.

I'd been thinking about ending this relationship, but I was anxious about the rumpus a split might cause. We'd broken up before, drifted back and now we were together out of habit. There was talk of us getting engaged. He didn't enjoy his low-grade office job and had a habit of denigrating my ambitions to be a drama teacher in front of other people. I suppose it made him feel better about himself. Alarm bells were ringing but I chose to ignore them until he phoned my college tutor to tell him I wouldn't be coming in the next day. I'd refused to skip my lectures to join him on a day off and this was an audacious attempt at control. We'd had a massive row over it, and this could have been my opportunity to end it, but still I lacked the courage.

The way things were going our respective families would eventually have to meet, and I knew that would be the beginning of the end. I had a recurring dream where, despite being divorced, Mum and Dad encounter Jeffrey's father for the first time. Mr Bigshot, as I liked to think of him, already comfortable in his favourite armchair, sits ready to grant Mum and Dad an audience. He does not rise to greet or welcome the visitors when they are shown in and after the introductions the rest of his family scatter like frightened rabbits. Not so much a meeting, more an awkward business interview follows.

In my fantasy, Mr Bigshot begins. "So, what do we, as a family stand to gain by allowing your daughter to marry our eldest son? What of value is she bringing to our great dynasty?"

My parents, sitting together on the plush velvet sofa opposite, look distinctly uncomfortable. Dad looks flustered and gives a nervous laugh before speaking.

"I, er, well, hmm. That's an unusual way to look at it, but, er, since you, ask..."

"Leslie, let me speak." At this point Mum rises from her seat, and Dad looks at her with an expression somewhere between

216

gratitude and fear. There's a dramatic pause and Mum's off, her voice rising an octave with each question.

"Gain? Value? What do you want from us? A herd of sheep as a dowry? Who the bloody hell do you think you're talking to, you jumped up, little nobody!" With that Mum grabs her handbag, uttering a colourful Yiddish curse, meaning that Mr Bigshot needs to search for the nearest lake to jump into. With a final toss of her head she's out the door, thereby denying Mr Bigshot the satisfaction of a reply, Dad following sheepishly in her wake. I always woke from this dream, relieved it was all over. Only it wasn't.

This was how I saw it going though, based on what I'd already observed at their dinner table. Staring at my plate in embarrassment I'd be forced to listen as someone was singled out for criticism for using too much petrol, adding unnecessary mileage to one of the many cars they had, squandering money-making opportunities, expecting handouts, eating too much or not eating enough. My normally over-confident boyfriend was reduced to a stammering wreck in his father's presence but nevertheless had the capacity to be just as domineering towards me, given half a chance.

Maybe some of my close friends guessed how unhappy I was, but mostly I hid my feelings and was selective with what I shared with Mum over the phone. I wanted to give the impression that everything was ticking along nicely without her.

She always rang in the morning when she knew Dad had left for work. She rang a lot. The calls were designed to keep the lines of communication open now she was living with David. Eventually, both my parents replaced the other with a new model.

Random strangers that I had neither chosen, nor wanted in my life, suddenly had to be considered, respected and even cared about. It was a tall order for me. I was struggling with the cleaning and these kinds of thoughts when Mum rang one morning.

"Hi, it's me. Well?"

She sounded awkward and I didn't do much to help the conversation along. "Well what?"

"You sound like you're busy."

"Yeah well I am. Someone has to clean this house," I said with a passive aggressive sniff.

There was a pause before she tried another tactic. "You ought to tell your father to get a cleaner," she ventured. "How can you do it all with your college work as well?" The glimmer of sympathy in the question took me by surprise, bursting the dam. Through tears, the stuff lying just beneath the surface came tumbling out. The time it took to keep everything clean and how it never seemed quite clean enough, no matter what I did and how I wanted it to stop.

When I finished, there was a sigh and a sound which signalled a kind of recognition, as if I'd just described the symptoms of an illness that she had too.

It was much more than just the cleaning that was getting to me of course. It was Dad's single status that was causing me anguish but I didn't mention that at this stage.

She promised to talk to Dad herself about advertising locally for a cleaner and we did eventually find one. A local housewife with her own family came to us every Saturday morning. If she wasn't already taken, no doubt Dad would be making a play for her too. Instead, he'd settled on Shirley. A married woman with children of her own. She never had a chance. I made sure of that.

The relationship had been going a few weeks when Dad brought her over to the house. He had this silly smile on his face when he introduced her.

"Hello, how very nice to meet you," she said offering her hand. In the other she held an oblong gift box. "This is for you. Happy Birthday."

Dad must have told her I'd turned twenty the week before. I couldn't find it in myself to even make eye contact with this woman standing in our hallway in her red woollen dress, but I managed to make the right noises. Dad ushered her through to the kitchen. I could hear them laughing and the sound of running water as he filled the kettle.

Out of sight I opened the box. It contained a decorative gilt ball point. A gift that had been carefully chosen. It was pretty. She was pretty, perhaps a little older than Mum, with wavy blond hair framing her face and a curvaceous figure. Her voice and smile were soft and kind, motherly even. There was nothing about her to dislike, but I did, with a passion. How dare she be with my Dad, in our kitchen. The way they looked at each other made me nauseous.

It must have been a week or so later when I headed back from college earlier than usual. Perhaps a lecture had been cancelled that day. Whatever the reason, it was unusual for me to be putting the key in the door, mid-afternoon. There seemed to be something wrong with the lock, though. The key wouldn't turn. I stood there baffled and tried again. How odd. I took a step back, unsure what to do. Ah, it doesn't matter. Dad's home. There's his car, large as life in the driveway. Still the penny didn't drop, even after I rang the bell and waited and waited.

Textured glass panels in the front door gave a wavy view of the hall and stairs from outside and eventually, human shapes appeared to be descending to ground level. There was a click as the latch was lifted and the door opened. Two flushed faces and crumpled clothing. I looked from one to the other in disbelief, inwardly cursing my own stupidity and their carelessness.

"Back from college, early?" muttered Dad, not meeting my stare. Shirley had crept away to the kitchen where I could see her, compact in hand, replenishing her lipstick. Mum's open plan scheme had led to the eventual removal of all the downstairs doors, so there was effectively nowhere to hide.

"Evidently," I snapped, moving past him to go upstairs.

I told Mum of course. She made a grim snorting noise down the phone as if passionate daytime sex and Dad didn't belong in the same sentence.

It wasn't just a stupid indiscretion on his part. A woman had turned his head and he didn't think twice about locking me out of the house. How long would it be before a woman persuaded him to lock me out of his life?

2

Dad, decent man that he was, decided to end his relationship with Shirley. He said he didn't want to be responsible for taking a mother away from her children. It transpired she had five of them. I pictured her brood as a line-up of different heights and genders, like the Von Trapps. We'd all had a lucky escape, but I was just relieved that I'd seen the last of her lurking around our house, and the pair of them behaving like hormonal teenagers.

From afar, Mum rejoiced with me on the phone. "Thank God, it's over. Five children? How did he think that was ever going to work?' If he's the one that's ended it, perhaps it's a sign that your father has come to his senses."

Mum and Dad still spoke to each other, mainly about practical matters relating to us, but I knew she'd make her views on this romance known to him. A few days later I heard him sheepishly agreeing over the phone that, yes, she was right, it was never going to work, that he should to have put a stop to it sooner than he did.

It didn't take him long to replace the buxom Shirley, but at first the new woman was a mystery, because she lived outside London, and a more formal courtship process was taking place. I learned that an introduction had been made through a distant relative. This developed into Dad making regular trips to a seaside town to see a widow called Dina. As the weeks went by, he gradually fed me morsels of tender, juicy information, just to let me know where this was going.

It was a Wednesday night. We were both at the kitchen table eating dinner when he brought up the subject, imitating what he thought passed for casual conversation.

"Dina's a very nice lady. Jewish. She's been through a lot. Nursed her husband at home herself when he got cancer," he said, cutting the meat on his plate into a tidy square.

I continued chewing, pretending to be fascinated by my dinner, but inwardly seething, at the way these details were left dangling in the air, willing me to care.

He blundered on. "It must have been very hard for her, watching her husband decline and then having to face life on her own. They didn't have any children."

I squashed the two stray peas in the middle of my plate with my fork and pushed the plate away.

"She always wanted children though, especially a daughter."

My left eyelid flickered, and the fingernails on one hand dug into the fleshy part of my palm.

Then the killer line. "She's very wealthy, actually."

I was clearly being buttered up for presentation as 'the daughter'. The inference being that I'd better not muck it up for Dad because it was quite important for the future of this relationship that she liked me and eventually, my brother too. I hated her already and we'd only just begun this journey.

Dad confided in Mum, but he had his own agenda. There was more than a hint of pleasure in his voice when he dropped in the bit about wealth. The money, apparently, came from several properties she owned and rented out. If Mum knew I was going to meet Dina she'd be pumping me for every detail afterwards.

The day of reckoning came, and as I was my mother's daughter, I selected my outfit with calculated care. Let her scrutinise and judge. Let her dare. I needed to feel supremely confident in my own skin. A dress that flattered, make-up not overdone, hair freshly washed and styled. Neat shoes with a small heel, matching handbag. Leather. I'd show her.

"Very smart," said Dad with a smile. He looked proud.

On a tree-lined avenue of grand houses, Dad slowed the car to pull into a sweeping double driveway between two pillars, guarded on each side by basking, plaster lions. A large detached house loomed over us. Dad rang the bell and when the chimes eventually stopped, he gave a little chuckle at the sing-song female response from behind the door.

"Com-ING! Dina's com-ING and here, I AM!"

The door flew open and a thin, elderly woman with an ash blonde permanent wave and thick foundation, beamed down at us both, arms open wide. She looked a lot older than Dad, but it was hard to judge because everyone said Dad didn't look his age.

"Hel-LO, dar-LING," she said, and to Dad, "you didn't tell me you had such a beautiful daughter!"

She ignored my horrified silence, pulling me over the threshold into the hall. Out of the corner of my eye I saw Dad hovering, ready to present a box of chocolates, but suddenly both her arms went around me, and she was planting kisses on both my cheeks as if we already knew each other. I was revolted by her intimacy and felt my body turn from flesh and blood to wood at her touch. At close quarters, she smelt of cheap perfume and mothballs.

"What are we doing lingering in the hall? Come through, come through," she said, accepting Dad's gift with a forced laugh.

As we both followed in her wake, I glanced at the staircase curving upwards to my left. Decorative red rope, such as you might find forming a barrier at VIP events, was attached to the wall. We made our way across a swirling pattern of red carpet, through a glass panelled door to a sitting room.

The pretentiousness of the plaited rope, the plaster lions in the driveway and this simpering, sugary woman put me in mind of something I couldn't quite put my finger on.

We were urged to take a seat on a couch with blue embossed covers. It felt synthetic to the touch. There was a faint, but non-specific aroma of something cooking in the background. Lunch, she told us was in the oven and would be ready shortly. Dad asked if he could help.

"Ooooh no, no, NO Les! I'M looking after YOU!" she cried in a no-arguing-with me-kind of tone. "No cooking duties for you today. You put your feet up after that long drive and don't you DARE get up."

Dad smiled in embarrassment. He wasn't used to sitting on his hands when it came to food preparation. It must have felt odd to have someone cooking for him but perhaps he enjoyed the novelty. She'd better be a good cook. I was hungry and in the habit of eating decent food. I knew my attitude was outrageous but in my eyes, Dina had a lot to prove and so far, I wasn't impressed. More than that, everything about her made me suspicious.

224

To stimulate conversation, she mentioned my performing arts studies. At my age, she was just the same. Not drama, but music. I raised a haughty eyebrow in her direction but undeterred, she produced from a drawer an album of black and white images of herself, in jaunty pose, playing a piano accordion. They must have been taken several decades ago judging from her appearance. Dad made all the right noises as he turned the pages of the album. I looked at them both, heads together, as they went through an accompanying folder of loose photos on the coffee table. Then, from a recess at the far end of the room, she brought out the actual accordion, strapping it on to demonstrate her singing repertoire with a few excruciating extracts. The vision was reminiscent of Bette Davis in *Whatever Happened to Baby Jane?* That's what I'd been struggling to remember.

Thankfully, she broke off to fetch Dad the cup of tea he'd agreed to. As she headed for the kitchen, she invited me to look around. "Upstairs, there's a games room with a snooker table that belonged to my late husband. Go and have a look, it's the first room on the right, dar-LING."

"Right." A room especially for the playing of games. Wealthy people seemed to have rooms in their houses that I'd never heard of. Jeffrey's family had one they called the 'morning room', where they only ate breakfast.

I took the opportunity to escape and followed the curving VIP rope upstairs. A full-sized snooker table and associated accessories didn't make much of an impression on me and I was soon bored.

The door to the room opposite was ajar and I glanced in. It was a bathroom. Every object in this room, from the bath to the towels was a homage to *Barbie* pink plastic and nylon. In the centre spot of the windowsill sat a knitted doll, dressed in an enormous pink skirt with frilled edges. The doll's skirt was the hideously coy cover for the spare toilet roll, pink of course. Even to my untrained eye, every item in the room looked the cheapest, tasteless example of its kind. Interior design by Woolworths. I took it all in. Mum would want to know about this. Just then I was summoned.

"Coo-EE. Dar-LING. Lunch is rea-DEE."

It was a show-off, three course, look-what-I-can-do effort that began with bean and barley soup. Greasy and heavy. Even as it went down, I predicted wanting to throw it up later, but I managed enough to look polite. The roast chicken and the accompaniments were passable. Baked potatoes and rice, steamed carrots and French beans. It could all have done with more seasoning and a few herbs for my liking. Dad was very complimentary though. Everything kosher, she boasted. Dad nodded, impressed. I was disgusted by his hypocrisy. Since when, did we care about kosher, pork eaters that we were! If only she knew. Dessert was a pineapple pudding with her 'special' non-dairy sauce, a gloopy sweet concoction and a poor substitute for a dollop of whipped cream or thick custard, neither of which is permitted after eating meat, according to Jewish dietary laws.

We all helped to clear the table and I followed her into the kitchen with the last of the dishes. Dad was in the back garden, admiring the flowers.

"It won't take me a minute to rinse these things," she said, "why don't you go and enjoy the sunshine with your father?"

The thought of some fresh air was quite appealing, but I remained rooted to the spot, fascinated by the back of her head. As she bent towards the dishes at the sink, the light from the window gave her hair a doll-like sheen. It seemed to curl away from the nape of her neck in a peculiar way, revealing backing material. Dina was wearing a wig.

After lunch, she insisted that we all took a stroll along the sea front. It was a mild day, but this was England so a walk along the promenade would be windy. She'd put on a cream three quarter length coat, a pink woollen scarf and was ready to go. On the lapel of her coat sat a rectangular brooch of blue and white stones. It was hard to miss.

"What a lovely brooch," said Dad, as she closed the front door behind us.

She looked up, her red lips puckered, the crease of a frown forming between her eyes.

"It was my mother's," she said, a protective hand hovering over it. She stood there, glaring at us both, as if we had threatened to rip it from her coat. After a moment she rearranged her face and gave a laugh, as if the peculiar overreaction was just her little joke.

Dad didn't appear to notice. He was already striding towards the car to collect our coats. If only he'd paid more attention. Before he married her.

3

It was a summer evening but still light outside. It must have
been around seven. I couldn't look at my watch because
that would risk being seen. I was on the floor of the lounge, eyes
closed, my back curving into the bay window and my cheek
pressed into the carpet, hardly daring to breathe.

Jeffrey had stopped banging on the window but I could feel
his presence, both hands against the glass, looking for signs of life
beyond the net curtains. My heart was pounding and one of my
legs felt like a dead weight. I was straining to hear a car door slam
and an engine start. Anything that would tell me he'd finally given
up and was driving off.

I'd told him in a phone call it was over. I tried to explain kindly
that I wasn't ready to get engaged. Fine, we could wait, he said.
No, I don't think that would work. I think we should finish. He
pleaded but I stood firm. Then the accusations. Who had I met?
It was someone at THAT drama school, wasn't it? I lied. No one
at college. No one anywhere. There *was* someone at college but
coming clean would escalate the problem. He'd only turn up there
and make a scene. I'm coming over so we can talk this out
properly, he said. The line went dead before I had a chance to
protest. I was alone in the house. I had to hide, quickly.

I made sure the door was locked and the chain on. There was no route around the house, but I checked the back door was secure anyway. I was about to draw the lounge curtains when I saw the car swerve round the corner at speed. I ducked down, hoping I hadn't been seen.

Dad had moved out and married Dina months before, and under her spell, he was lost to me. It's kids that are supposed to leave home, not the parents, I joked to my friends. Laughing at myself was one way to avoid dwelling on the hurt. The grim reality was me, lying on the floor of my own home, alone and fearful, while my parents played happy families elsewhere.

Jeffrey was heavy on his feet and I could hear his shoes making contact with the ground as he paced up and down. There was a pause and a click from his lighter as he lit another cigarette. Then I heard him shouting through the letter box.

"I know you're in there, just answer the door and face me!" He sounded so aggressive. I put my hands over my ears and held my breath.

I must have fallen asleep because when I woke up, the room was dark, and I was shivering. It took me a few moments to work out where I was and why. I couldn't be sure he wasn't still outside, so I crawled, snake-like, out of the room and up the stairs. As I reached the top, the phone rang. Leaving it to ring and ring in the darkness ramped up my anxiety levels. I pictured him hanging on, impatiently tapping the ash from his cigarette into the cut glass ash tray, on the hall table at his parent's house. Eventually it dawned on me that if he was phoning from home, he couldn't still be outside.

Crouching down at the bedroom window, I cautiously pulled back the edge of the net curtain and looked outside. The streetlight showed a silent street. The next morning I ran to the station, looking over my shoulder all the way. I had a bag with me. I'd have to hide out with Mum and David. There was nowhere else I could go.

******

It was the school summer holidays. My brother had been invited to spend time with Dad and Dina on the coast, so I knew his room at Mum and David's flat could be my bolthole. It was a comfortable flat, in a leafy suburb. David was the financial director of a furniture company. I'd explained what had happened the previous night to Mum on the phone.

"I always said he had an arrogant, unpleasant side. I've never understood why you were so frightened of the father, though." she said, "You're quite capable of sticking up for yourself." There was a pointed tone to this remark.

"You don't understand. You haven't met the father. Everyone walks on eggshells round him. Anyway, that's beside the point. I should've ended it sooner." I didn't say this but for a long time I'd told myself that maintaining long-term relationships relied on at least one of the parties feeling discontented most of the time.

I don't remember the first time I met David but knowing how angry I was about my parent's separation back then, I'm sure I came across as surly and unforgiving. I would have given clipped answers to basic pleasantries and revelled in my mother's obvious discomfort at my sullen attitude. I was never going to make it easy for her by just falling in line and she knew it. David, like Dina, had much to prove, but they were from different planets. He had young adult children of his own, and understood the patience required to keep those relationships on an even keel through difficult changes. I don't suppose it was any easier for his children to accept my mother's arrival in their father's life either. Dina, on the other hand, regarded us as decorative items that she could pick up and play with when it suited her. Much as she boasted about her new family, she cherry picked the aspects of family life that were to her liking. That summer she sent my thirteen-year old brother back from her care with a fortnight's dirty laundry packed into bags for my mother's attention. It was never forgotten. I simply couldn't understand what Dad saw in her as a person.

David put in the work and little by little, his intelligence, sincerity and patience won me over. He had a way of giving me his full attention, breaking off in gales of laughter, mid-conversation at something I'd said that he found amusing or clever. He'd wanted to learn to play the cello as a boy, but his family couldn't afford to pay for lessons, so he poured his passion into the appreciation of classical music and had an encyclopaedic knowledge. When I was struggling to find the right music for a play I was directing at college, he gave the project careful thought and introduced me to Satie and Poulenc. The choice of music was important to me, and he cared about it too. He was never critical or judgemental and giving praise to others came easily to him.

I arrived before dinner. I wasn't used to seeing Mum prepare food but with David she had come to it on her own terms. Cooking was one of those activities that always threatened her fragile self-esteem, with Dad being a chef. She had a go at making a meat pie once, but somehow manged to season it with sugar rather than salt. Dad made much of her error and she fumed at his reaction. I watched, open-mouthed as she consulted a recipe book, made a tarragon-flavoured salad dressing and arranged lamb cutlets on our plates as if she'd been doing these things with flair for years. I didn't remark on this or say anything tasted good. David did though.

When I was growing up there was a constant tension between Mum's inclination to overindulge and Dad's ability to produce abundant, delicious portions. It was a hard balance to strike, and as I grew into a short, plump adult, with a love of good food, I felt it too. Poor Dad often got the blame for our collective weight gain.

We'd just finished dinner on the second night of my stay when we heard the screech of tyres on asphalt. The kitchen overlooked a private car park for the residents in the block. David looked out of the window first.

"Looks like we might have a visitor," he said to me. I looked out and saw the car and my stomach lurched. Dark blue Hillman Imp and a grim-faced, heavy figure stubbing out a cigarette on the ground. He locked the car and disappeared from our view. The entry phone would sound any minute.

"Right, we'd better hear what he has to say. He's obviously got something he needs to get off his chest," said Mum, rather generously I thought. The entry phone buzzed, and Mum went to the hall to pick it up. We heard her say, "Yes, she's here. Yes, she is upset. Yes, I realise that but I'm not sure she wants to see *you*. Look I'm not arguing with you, like this. Just hold on a minute." We'd followed her out to the hall. She put her hand over the receiver and looked at us. "Well, do I let him in?" she whispered.

She had a mischievous look on her face as if this was all a bit of a lark.

David nodded. "Let me answer the door," he said to me, a reassuring hand on my shoulder. I fled to the lounge with Mum. The doorbell sounded and we heard the exchange. They'd met before.

"Hello David. I know she's here. I need to talk to her. Tell her to come out to the car," said a familiar voice.

"I'll do no such thing," we heard David say. "What you need to say can be said here but you'll remain civil or you're out. Do I make myself clear?" There was an authority in David's tone that I hadn't heard before. It felt protective. Jeffrey was shown in. His bulk filled the armchair. I sat on the sofa opposite. David and Mum hovered nearby, comfortably within earshot.

"Well, are you going to explain yourself?" he began. "I don't understand what I'm supposed to have done. That's why I'm here. To hear your side of it," he said. The words were self-pitying, the expression hard-done-by but the body language said something else. He leaned back, crossed his legs and folded his arms, as if he planned on staying the whole night if that's what it took to get the answers he'd come for.

I stared at my lap and took a breath. "I'm sorry if you're upset but it just doesn't feel right for me anymore. There's nothing more I can say."

He leaped up and towered over me, his face contorted in anger. "That's it, is it? Is that all you can say? You bloody bitch, you!" He broke off in shock when he felt David grab his arm. "Get your hands off me," he said pulling away.

"That's it now. Sling your hook, I've heard enough," said David. "Time to leave, and the door's this way." David maintained a firm grip and led him out, still protesting. I heard Jeffrey swear and David saying an emphatic goodbye just before the door closed.

David turned to Mum "You alright darling?" He called Mum 'darling' or 'dolly' a lot. She nodded, smiling in a grim, what-have-we-just-witnessed kind of way.

I stared at them both, still trying to absorb what had just taken place. Mum broke the silence. "Well, what a hoo-ha that was! I think we could all do with a cup of tea."

We spent the rest of the evening dissecting the whole encounter, analysing how quickly Jeffrey had lost his composure and congratulating David on the way he took control of the situation. We speculated about how he might present his account to his parents, our laughter helping to diffuse the tension.

Despite my unforgiving nature, something changed for me that night. Mum and David had been there for me when I needed help.

I stayed away from home for the rest of that summer. Our house was put up for sale and a flat was purchased from the proceeds, so I had somewhere to live. Jeffrey didn't know the address.

4

There were family occasions when my parents, though divorced still had to show up with their respective new partners and be polite to each other. Dad and David managed these situations quite well, but Mum and Dina were like coiled springs if forced to be in the same space for too long. For one thing, Dina was very suspicious of Mum and jealous that she and Dad still communicated on issues affecting his children. For her part, Mum despised Dina's alleged penny-pinching, despite her alleged wealth. There had been some frank exchanges about Dad's meagre financial support for my brother, who was still at school.

Mum had this theory that Dad had to justify every telephone conversation that took place between them because Dina begrudged the cost of the calls. We spent many hours on the phone speculating about this.

"How can you possibly know that she's jealous of Dad speaking to you?" I asked her.

"I know, because if he takes a call downstairs and she's upstairs, she listens in on the extension. I can hear the click when she picks up. If she's just in the next room, your father will suddenly and deliberately start talking very loudly so she can hear every word he says. It's so obvious she calls the shots in that house, especially over money. Didn't your father tell us that she walks for miles to save a penny here and there on groceries?" she said.

Mum could talk for hours along these lines, but yes, she was right. Dad had presented Dina's thriftiness as a virtue. To have a wife that cared more about saving than spending, was a certainly a departure from Mum.

A few months after David saw off my controlling boyfriend, I met my husband, Tim. His job in oil and gas exploration took him all over the world and when an opportunity to work in Australia for a few years presented itself, we decided to get married before he had to go. We couldn't leave the UK together as my teaching job required a term's notice. When the day finally came for me to fly out, everyone came to the airport to see me off. Airports are exciting places for travellers, the starting point for the adventure, but for people going nowhere they have all the allure of a dental appointment. Unless you happen to be a plane spotter, like my brother.

I was about to disappear to the other side of the world, where the husband I hadn't seen for three months, was waiting for me to arrive. I couldn't wait to go through the gate and leave them all to get on with their lives without me, but the torture of the airport café had to be endured first. It was crowded and the only table that could accommodate us all had bench seating on one side.

The men had gone to the counter to get cups of tea that none of us wanted. I'd sat down on one end of the bench, within sight of the flight information board. While Dina kept her eyes fixed on Dad in the queue, I watched Mum inspecting every detail of Dina's appearance, making judgements about the quality of her clothes and the obvious signs of age in her face. I could always tell exactly what Mum was thinking, just by her expression, but one of her unfiltered comments was about to ram the point home. She'd come to the airport, dressed to kill. She pointed to the bench with a friendly smile. "Come along Dina, you go in the middle, you're skinny enough to fit in that tiny space." She said 'skinny' as if it was a disease.

Dina's expression darkened and she narrowed her eyes. Mum pretended not to notice. "Do you mind?" she countered. "Skinny? Perhaps you'd better go on the end then – fatty!"

Mum gave her a withering look and I thought I heard her mutter, 'bloody cheek' but then Dad and David came back with trays and the tea was distributed, amid an undercurrent of female hostility and stilted conversation about the duration of the flight and the likely temperature in Adelaide. I opted not to extend the agony by waiting for my flight to be called. When I said I'd better go through, an unmistakable sense of relief hovered over our party. They each hugged me in turn, and we said our goodbyes. Later, Mum told me that she and David lingered, watching me walk away, hoping I'd look back, but I kept on walking.

I gave birth to our first son when we returned to the UK, three years later. Despite my hurt at Mum and David not coming to Australia when we were there, they were close at hand when they became grandparents. Dad didn't know he was a grandfather until two weeks after the event. He and Dina had booked a holiday around the due date. It felt deliberate on her part.

"Why didn't you at least leave us the contact details for your hotel," I sobbed, when he returned. "We could have rung. Everyone knew, except you."

"We just didn't think about it because it would have been terribly expensive for you to call overseas."

"I wouldn't have cared about the cost! The cost? How often do I get a chance to say you have a grandson?"

He didn't have an answer. He'd sold his soul to Dina.

******

Soon after our second son was born, we moved to a bigger house that had once been two separate cottages. It wasn't a great purchase. Our new home was like a sickly child in constant need of medical attention. No sooner did we fix one leak than we'd find water dripping from a radiator or through a ceiling somewhere else. The garden, perfect for children, had a large overgrown lawn, but money was tight, and we didn't have the spare cash for a lawnmower.

The phone rang one Sunday morning as it always did. It was Dad and after a few superficial pleasantries he said he was handing over to Dina. I'd got used to having these weekly minimal exchanges with him by this time. We just didn't have much to say to each other anymore. I let her gush. There was no choice. "Hel-LO, dar-LING, it's Dina here. How are the boys?" She didn't wait for the answer. "Good, good. I told your father I particularly wanted to speak to you myself, to find out what I can buy you for the house. What can I pay for? What do you need?"

"Thank you, that's very kind. I'm not sure, well, um, we could do with a lawnmower really, but we haven't looked at any specifically..." She cut me off.

"Well you go and have a look at what you'd like, and you just let me know," she said. It sounded very generous on her part and

I said so, but I had my misgivings about accepting an expensive gift that made us beholden to her. Her words carried a subtle message not lost on me. '*I'd* like to buy, not '*we*'. The birthday cards, money clipped inside, were always written in her loopy scrawl. Dad always told us to thank her for the money, not him. I got used to the annual reminder not to forget her birthday a week before the date. As if he couldn't trust us not to embarrass him. It always left me with the uncomfortable feeling that he would be in the doghouse if we failed to come up to scratch.

We concluded the call soon after and I replaced the receiver. Less than a minute later I tried to make another call and as I started to dial, I heard Dina's voice coming out of the earpiece. It took me a moment to realise she hadn't replaced the receiver properly and the line was still open. I pressed at my end to clear it but instead of the dialling tone I just heard Dina the real Dina, saying what she really thought of us. Her nasty words were being broadcast loud and clear from her kitchen to mine.

"A lawnmower, if you please! That's the trouble with your children, Leslie. Always out for what they can get. Well not from me. I won't have it. I'm not wasting all that money, *my* money, on a lawnmower. How dare she even suggest it." I listened, horrified at first and then with grim amusement. This was dynamite. What were the chances that she'd be caught out like this?

She wasn't talking to herself though. I pictured how Dad, head down, would be shifting uncomfortably in his chair at these remarks. I waited and waited for him to say something in our defence, but he remained silent while she ranted on. The peculiar nature of their relationship gave her the right to express these views, privately to him, whilst keeping up a public pretence that she loved the family that she'd acquired. We purchased our own lawnmower and a gift was never mentioned again but, we had to endure many more years of her hypocrisy before the inequality of their relationship was revealed. I've no doubt she loved and cared for Dad while she had the upper hand on all decision-making but after she'd had a stroke and was lying helpless in a hospital bed, wig slightly askew, the reality was grim.

I arrived at the ward to see Dad bending over her bed, so his face was in her line of sight. There had been no improvement in her condition since her admission the week before. Her eyes were open but lifeless. Occasionally we would see movement of her limbs under the bedclothes and she sometimes turned her head from side to side. That's when he tried talking to her.

"Dina darling. It's Les. I need to ask you something." He was as close to her face as the hospital bed allowed and he spoke in a whisper so the nurses passing by wouldn't hear. "I haven't got any money, darling. I can't pay for anything. Where's the bank book?" He waited for an answer, but she just looked beyond him with an unblinking stare.

Had they never discussed, 'what happens if?' Dad tried to convince me that she just didn't think like that. Yes, she did, I thought. She knew only too well that she had total control of all her money and apparently Dad's small pension too. Being incapacitated, or dying before he did, just wasn't in her masterplan. I knew I would never forgive her for making Dad beg for scraps at her bedside but there was worse to come.

After several months of illness, Dina died. She'd made a will but had not discussed the content with Dad, so it came as a shock to him that she'd left the bulk of her estate to two distant relatives

240

that by all accounts she despised. Her bequest to Dad was the roof over his head but no means of paying for the costs of continuing to live in it. In his eighties, Dad had no choice but to sell quickly and move to more affordable accommodation.

It was when he was packing up in preparation for completion on the house that he came across a small white box, hidden in the niche of an upstairs cupboard. Inside was a large brooch of blue and white stones, the same brooch he'd admired on Dina's coat all those years ago. He hadn't seen it since.

The next time he was in the town he took it to a smart jeweller's shop. The man behind the counter was charming. He gave the item his full attention, taking out his eyeglass and turning the item this way and that. Satisfied, he returned the brooch to the box, handing it back to Dad with an apologetic smile.

"This may not be what you are expecting to hear. This is very cleverly made but the stones are nothing more than glass, I'm afraid. Totally worthless of course, but I can see how you were fooled."

When he told me about this episode, at our kitchen table in Yorkshire, he chuckled over it. His refusal to see Dina in anything other than a positive light made me bold.

"One thing I'd love to know, Dad. Why did you never stand up to her?"

He looked at something over my shoulder for a few moments before replying. "She was my wife," he said at last.

"But we are your children." He didn't have an answer.

******

Dad moved to a modest but comfortable flat in a purpose-built block for elderly people. He didn't stay lonely for long. He looked at least ten years younger than his age and could still turn a woman's head with restaurant quality cooking for two at his kitchen table. It was only a matter of time.

The sale of the house had left him with a little to spare. Probably for the first time in his life, he had complete control over his own money, but he was a soft touch. A name started to pepper his conversation. Companionship, someone to share a meal with, go on outings, holidays perhaps. The opera. Just a nice little old lady, said my brother after we'd met her. I wasn't so sure. A few months later Dad suffered a stroke after an evening out with his new companion. He lay in a hospital bed, unconscious for three days. On the second day the consultant showed us the brain scan. The areas of darkness revealed the extent of the bleeding, and the words no relative wants to hear. 'I'm afraid there's no hope.' He probably said how sorry he was, but I didn't register it.

Dad was unconscious but breathing on his own. According to the experts, he had the heart and lungs of a much younger man. As we sat by his bed, hour upon hour listening to him draw breath, it was like looking at an abandoned car. The engine was still running but the driver had gone. His face looked exactly as it always did in repose. Sometimes he coughed, giving the illusion that he'd just dozed off and would wake up in a few minutes. But he never did. Mum came to the hospital and said a private goodbye. She wept. Their marriage may have ended but they didn't hate each other. Early in the morning on the third day my brother and I were preparing to drive back to the hospital when the call came. When we went in to see him for the last time, the

242

change in his appearance was shocking. Overnight his hair had turned completely white. He'd dodged the process of aging until the very last moments of life.

We were still in the very early stages of coming to terms with his death when I had a call from his solicitor. Had I known that months before, Dad had made an appointment to see him that afternoon? No, I didn't, but how sad that he couldn't keep it. He told me an elderly woman, a friend of Dad's apparently, had turned up in his place.

"Really? Why?" I was starting to feel uneasy even before he told me her name. At this point we knew he'd planned to go on a cruise with her. A cruise we knew he'd paid for.

The solicitor continued. "She's claiming your father intended to leave her ten thousand pounds and furthermore, she says if circumstances had been different, he planned to add this instruction to his will." The room was spinning. I heard the caller clear his throat. "There is nothing in writing of course but she is asking if you and your brother will consider honouring, what she believes, was your father's last wish. I told her I would put it to you."

Oh, Dad. What was it with you and women?

5

North Yorkshire, 1990s

I'd wandered into my own lounge to find none of the furniture was in its usual place.

"What exactly do you think you're doing?"

David, balancing a television in his arms, looked like he'd been caught stealing and Mum, in the centre of the chaos appeared miffed at being interrupted before the grand plan was unveiled.

"Why are both the sofas on one side of the room?" I looked at Mum for answers.

"Just be quiet a minute and let me concentrate," said Mum, frowning. "I'm trying to decide where the television should go."

"Excuse me, how would *you* feel if I came to your house and started moving the furniture around?" She looked at me as if this proposition was beyond her understanding.

"I've always thought this room is a very awkward shape so I'm experimenting with a different arrangement," she said, standing there, hands on hips, surveying the scene as if it was obvious that her help was required. She was in her own clumsy way, attempting to lend a hand. She was right. There was no obvious way to arrange our furniture that felt comfortable, but I could work it out myself, if and when and I chose to do so, and without her interference.

"We are quite capable of deciding where to put our own furniture if you don't mind," I said. "I'd like it put back just the way it was, thank you. Move your own furniture if you must but leave mine alone."

"Keep your hair on," rang in my ears as I left the room, fuming.

I heard David murmuring to Mum from the hall. "I told you this was a bad idea, Sylvia."

"Oh, alright, don't you go on, as well. I can't seem to say or do anything right. You see what I mean? When I try to get close to her, she just pushes me away."

"Perhaps this isn't the way to do it. Not everyone has to toe your line, dolly," said David in his soothing, kindly way. Too right.

My husband Tim was invariably shocked by the way Mum and I talked to each other. The confrontational, all guns blazing approach took some getting used to. I'd explained it was a Jewish thing, laughing it off, through gritted teeth.

At least our third house move, to a beautiful North Yorkshire town, had her blessing, even if it was a four-hour drive from London. An abundance of smart independent boutiques catering for the well-heeled, mature woman and old-style personal service never failed to impress. Even the supermarkets, she insisted were better stocked than the ones she used. "I could live here," she said, at least once during every visit, with an enthusiasm that made me nervous.

Yesterday, she'd arrived at the door, leaving David to carry the bags in from the car as usual. While he was willingly dragged off to play by our two boys, Mum presented her cheek for a dutiful kiss and then an inspection of the premises and my appearance began. According to Mum I wore too much black and I decorated my home with too much blue. Walking from room to room, she threw out the opinions and random observations I hadn't asked for, without any idea how crushing they were to me. It was her idea of intimacy, but I didn't see it like that.

"I would never have chosen Venetian blinds. Such a nightmare to keep clean. I wish I was so casual about housework, like you are."

I showed her to a bedroom without a speck of blue in the décor. "Ooh, a room that isn't blue! What happened?" I heard. She loved a bit of sarcasm.

Downstairs, I declined a slice of the lemon cake I'd made for the visitors and waited for the predictable response.

"Enough with the dieting. You've lost too much weight. Your neck looks scraggy."

On a previous visit it was, "You've put on a few pounds. That dress looks very clingy at the back."

On some level, I always fell short in her eyes. Always needed improvement. She didn't mean her comments to be taken that way but the cumulative, pointed remarks about my homemaking, my appearance, me as an individual, had a corrosive effect. I always rose to the bait. Despite my apparent shortcomings, Tim and I were secure in each other and we had created a happy little family. Perhaps I was capable of doing something right, despite what she thought.

If I was quick to react and appeared hyper-sensitive, I'd had a good teacher, and looking back I could be just as hurtful too. I hadn't invited her and David to my 40th birthday party, making the excuse that Dad and Dina weren't invited either. I could hear the sadness in her voice when I told her, but the truth was I just

246

didn't want her there. She would have made the event all about her and I was fearful of being belittled in front of my friends. I regret that now. She would have enjoyed seeing how excited our boys were at being part of the adult's fun. We had caterers and a marquee. It was just the sort of dressed-up occasion she would have loved, and she should have been there. If I'd invited Dad and Dina, doubtless their presence would have created more unwanted tension. It was all so complicated.

For years Mum led an amateur musical theatre group as a hobby, organising the choreography of a dozen performers, often in limited spaces. Their shows raised hundreds of pounds for worthy causes. If pressed, I would see them perform from time to time and would compliment one or other of the group but always, held back on enthusing about Mum's performance. I just couldn't bring myself to say what she wanted to hear. She always chose to sing sassy, comic numbers and could put them across well. I was the arts writer for a newspaper group at the time. Giving talented amateurs considered feedback and praise was my job. It was less emotionally complicated to give it to total strangers. Once or twice I took her along to a show at our local theatre, where her enjoyment helped to inform my review.

Our differences occasionally brought us together, though. If musical theatre was her great passion, then mine was drama. For years we had a running joke about Samuel Beckett after she'd typed out my college essays for submission to an examiner. From then on, she referred to *Happy Days*, as 'that mad play where a woman is buried up to her neck in sand'. Only we understood the reference and I took a certain pride in having extended her knowledge of literary genius.

We could spend hours on the phone, completely in tune with each other on Dad's gullibility and Dina's deceit. The solicitor that had helped us bat away the woman with a claim on Dad's will turned out to be less than professional himself. I'd sought advice from the legal regulatory authorities following his firm's refusal to explain the enormous charges accrued for administering Dad's very straightforward estate. From the evidence I produced, the complaint had been deemed, 'serious' and an investigation was under way. I had much to share with Mum on this issue and the twists and turns involved in fighting a crooked solicitor made for interesting conversations over many months.

I also became her closest confidante if someone in her social circle turned out to be a disappointment. The telephone conversation would start thus. "Have you got a minute? I want you to tell you something that's happened, and you tell me if I have good reason to be furious." A turn of phrase indicating that I could either give her the response that chimed with her own opinion or be prepared to engage in a very lengthy debate.

One time she outlined a transgression that cut to the very heart of her insecurities. A long-standing friend had secretly and deliberately purchased the same outfit as her. She obviously didn't count on being seen by a mutual acquaintance who wasted no time in breaking the news. I tried to calm the waters by pointing out that imitation is the greatest form of flattery, that the friend in question must have greatly admired Mum's taste but lacked the confidence to be open and straightforward. I felt sure there must be a way of communicating the disappointment to the guilty party without destroying the friendship entirely.

248

It all fell on deaf ears of course and I reverted to taking her side. It was easier. To Mum this was tantamount to identity theft and the secrecy with which the whole enterprise was carried out would never be forgotten or forgiven. Never in a million years.

Months later, peace talks were opened by the respective husbands, but these also came to nothing. The woman in question, who lived on the same street as Mum and David, had to be studiously avoided for evermore, with the possibility of accidental sightings at any time, further aggravating the feud.

This uncomfortable episode was by no means unique. It had played out in other ways all through my childhood. From time to time a woman would establish a relationship with Mum, socially or at work until there was a giant falling out. Mum naturally presented herself as the injured party, but I doubt she was always as blameless as she made out. She was extraordinarily unforgiving, reading a slight or a criticism into an innocent remark, yet capable herself of launching a tactless missile, that could leave the other party breathless at the cheek of it. For many years, and until her health declined, she worked on the costume jewellery counters of Harrods and Selfridges. Shortly after Live Aid, and well before the knighthood, Bob Geldof strolled by and Mum helped him choose a birthday gift for one of his daughters. During this encounter Mum apparently told the world's greatest charity fundraiser that it was about time he tidied himself up.

"I know, I really should," he said, with a grin, rubbing the stubble on his chin. She could get away with saying anything to a man and Bob Geldof was clearly under her spell that day. Women could bring out the worst in her, though. When I was a child, we had a succession of babysitters with one, a Mrs Norris, getting the sack in dramatic fashion in a most bizarre episode that could only have happened in our house. Mrs Norris was hired to look after my brother on the days Mum was at work and as I was mostly at school, she didn't really make much of an impression on me. She came to our house early in the mornings and all went along fine for a few months until Mum came back one day and detected Mrs Norris' curiosity had got the better of her. It appeared our babysitter had been having a sly look at the contents of Mum's wardrobes, not realising that the lady of the house would instantly know if a door had been opened in her absence. Moving any item so much as a centimetre from its designated position was tantamount to a signed confession. Mrs Norris had unfortunately left a trail of clues, indicating that she had an interest in the corsetry arrangements that helped Mum squeeze back into her pre-pregnancy office wear. With anyone else, Mrs Norris might have got away with it, but she crumbled under Mum's fierce interrogation and admitted that yes, she had looked through the wardrobes because she so admired Mum's style. With all trust gone, flattery and apologies got her nowhere, other than out the door.

I don't remember Dad having a view on this altercation but David, probably because he was at a stage in life where he could be ever present, was much more involved in all her dramas. He was protective of Mum, and all of us. He paid attention, remembered details and asked the right questions. There was no doubt he adored her, but he could be firm when required. Of the two, he appeared more vigorous, energetic and healthy. In later years his hearing declined, which often meant he would start a different conversation with one of us while Mum was also talking.

It was hard to know who to respond to first as they would both be talking at once and require different answers. It was an unintentional comedy act.

Mum suffered with pain and she didn't suffer in silence. Her back and feet gave her problems. She was diagnosed with trigeminal neuralgia, a notoriously painful condition. She had digestive problems, migraine, heart palpitations and took a cocktail of prescription drugs every day. David took on the role of carer so effectively we hardly knew how reliant she was on his strength, until he was no longer there.

They'd just returned from a holiday and were at home when he had the stroke. At first it looked like he would recover. When we arrived at the hospital he was conscious and alert. His speech was a little slurred but intelligent. He asked questions about the progress of my complaint against the solicitor and gave his usual hearty laugh at the news of a positive outcome after so many months of investigation. His right hand didn't seem to be functioning. As we looked round the ward at the other patients, motionless, unresponsive, close to death, we had every reason to believe David would pull through, but weeks at his hospital bed turned into months as his condition gradually worsened. He started to sleep for long periods and when he was awake, his speech was unintelligible. On Christmas Day he was wheeled into a day room and gave a speech of thanks to the nursing staff for their dedication and hard work but no one except Mum knew that's what he was saying. He died in Mum's arms in the second week of 2008.

6

The first time Mum came to stay with us after David died, she travelled up by train on her own, and somehow arrived without incident. On the second evening I was preparing dinner in the kitchen when a sound like thunder reverberated throughout the house. She'd fallen down the stairs and was lying still at the bottom, curled up, like a baby. I rushed to the hall, frantic, until her eyes opened, and she spoke. She was annoyed. A good sign.

"Your bloody stairs! I must have just slipped," she whispered, not moving. "Just let me lie her for a minute. I'll soon know if anything's broken." I was standing over her, exuding panic, shouting to Tim to call an ambulance.

"Just be quiet, will you and stop flapping. I'm going to go home black and blue from this. Everyone will think I've been beaten."

Finally, she let me help her sit up. Somehow, she lifted herself onto her knees and gradually to her feet. It was a miracle she came off so lightly.

The make-up couldn't disguise the black eye and she tried to make a joke of it in front of my dinner guests the next night. She still looked glamorous, despite the fall and my generous friends told her so.

I saw her onto the train back to London and lingered on the platform until the train departed. She'd told me to go home, saying there was no need to wait in the cold. She didn't want me to see her looking out of the window, defeated and lonely.

*****

The last time we went shopping together she clung on to my arm for support. She'd stubbornly refused to use a walking stick and we'd all given up trying to persuade her. A fear of looking elderly was the main objection.

We headed towards the shopping centre, joined at the arm. Her right, my left. I struggled to walk as slowly as her and she sensed my frustration. I was practically pulling her along. Siamese twins must get used to each other's rhythm. We were never going to master it in less than an hour.

Inside we soon realised the effort was pointless. *Shlepping* ourselves around the fashion floor of her favourite department store meant we were both compelled to look at the same items. If we let go of each other, even for a moment, she might lose her footing. For a mother and daughter that rarely touched, never mind hugged, we were pathetically inseparable, and I wasn't sorry when she suggested we call it a day.

"Let's go to the bench outside. Leave me there and you come back and look round without me."

"I'm not looking for anything special. We can go if you've had enough."

"Yes, let's go home."

Walking had become a problem for her, but I was shocked at how unsteady she was. She still looked perfectly groomed, and could even be bothered to wear contact lenses, rather than giving in to glasses. We were just starting to get to know each other but it felt too late. The injustice of the situation irritated me. How dare she be old!

The day before I left for Dubai, I booked dinner for three at a restaurant she liked. Mum with her children. Just us. My treat.

It was a lovely evening. She could still eat with relish. Minestrone soup, steak, bread with thick butter, cheesecake. It was good to see, and I told her so.

"Ach, I'll probably be up all night with heartburn but what's new?"

We talked about everything except my imminent departure for Dubai. My brother's job, his girls, my boys. The wine.

"I don't want this evening to be goodbye," she said, suddenly, changing the direction of the conversation. I brushed off the obvious implication in her statement, that although I was only going to Dubai for two years, at her age, two years might be too long.

"The time will fly by. You'll see. And now you know how to Skype we can speak in person whenever you like – plus we'll have trips home at least once a year," I countered, rushing in to paper over the uncomfortable truth.

We talked about her taking a cruise to the Middle East once we'd settled. Maybe next year. Maybe. Her remark stayed in the air above our table. She sounded frightened and I was frightened for her.

Time to go. We needed to retrieve our coats from the stand at the entrance. I didn't think. Reaching for her coat, I momentarily let go of her arm and she collapsed behind me like a rag doll, the side of her face hitting the wooden floor.

"Oh, Mum, what happened?" we cried.

We both lifted her to a chair, mopping the blood from her lip. The manager offered brandy, but she waved it away, embarrassed by the attention and the disturbance to the other diners. Their nudges and nods said it all. At another table, a man within earshot commented to his wife.

"What a shame. Can you see, over there, by the coat stand? Poor old dear. That was a nasty fall. You should've seen how she hit the floor."

Her lip was swelling and a bruise on the side of her face already visible. The evening wasn't supposed to end like this, in fear for the goodbye to come.

******

I wondered if we'd find a letter addressed to us among her papers. Several years before he died, David secretly wrote one for her, setting down his deepest feelings and offering practical advice and guidance on what she should do when the time came. Perhaps it had prompted her to do something similar. In the end there was only the envelope containing her will and a bizarre instruction to add five years to the date of birth on her gravestone, so her friends wouldn't know that she lied about her age. Nothing more.

She'd been gone a year, but I couldn't let go so I made an appointment with a medium. She always knew I would, but maybe not that soon.

A commuter train delivered me from the outer suburbs to central London. I hardly noticed the journey and climbing the steps that took me from underground platform to daylight, present time evaporated.

When I was a teenager, at a loose end on a Saturday, I'd be drawn to my nearest Tube station and the gateway to adventure. Studying the London Underground map by the ticket office, excited by all its colour-coded possibilities, I'd pick a station, work out the route and just go there. Just to see the place behind the name. Barons Court, Seven Sisters, Temple. Evocative place names on lines that took me beyond the familiar northern reaches of the magenta Metropolitan line. Tube travel was relatively affordable then and it felt sophisticated and purposeful to be going somewhere. I never tired of exploring London on my own, negotiating my way to unknown destinations, picturing a different life for myself.

Sixteen-year-old me would have been disappointed with this destination, though. With no quirky shops or places of interest in immediate sight, I wouldn't have lingered. The only sign of life near the station's exit was a hopeful flower seller on the corner and a well-heeled woman with a yappy dog on a lead.

It was a sunny November morning and the mild temperature unusual for this time of year, so I slowed to a stroll and passed a trendy looking gastro pub at the end of the street. It was much too early in the day to be of much interest but its advertised promise of 'modern British food' was a reminder of the shift in tastes since the 1970s when prawn cocktail, sirloin steak and black forest gateau were dining out staples.

I turned into a grand crescent of white stuccoed period houses that once belonged to wealthy families and their servants but were now divided into fashionable apartments with million-pound price tags and top end rents. It looked like a film set but somewhere behind these elegant facades a woman I'd never met before was waiting for me to arrive. I passed the house and did a circuit round the block to waste another few minutes as I was too early. Impatient, I returned and rang the buzzer anyway.

It was an unremarkable hallway after the grandeur of the exterior. The lift delivered me to the third floor and another front door. I was nervous but quietly confident that this wouldn't be a wasted journey.

Mum and I had talked about these things at length. Both of us consulted psychics from time to time. Strangers with remarkable gifts that fed back to us meaningful and specific details of our lives, the people in them, some we'd lost, children and grandchildren not yet conceived. Too much to dismiss out of hand.

The idea that the wisdom and insight of fortune tellers, astrologers and the like could provide comfort and direction at a time of confusion and unhappiness started way back for Mum. On a family holiday at a seaside resort in Italy, a gypsy read her palm. She reported it all back to Dad in front of me. Never the slightest inhibition about what I might be overhearing. Children don't understand these things, or so she believed.

"That was interesting, Leslie. She said another man is going to come into my life and it'll be a very important relationship! She said my hand showed a great sadness. She could see it all. Remarkable."

Naturally, Dad humoured her, laughing off the idea that a palm-reading by a stranger in a seaside booth could carry such importance. Later I wondered if this prediction preyed on her mind in such a way that it in the end it became a self-fulfilling prophesy.

Long after she'd married the 'other man', the daily horoscope column in the favoured tabloid, was hailed as further confirmation of her beliefs. Vague generalisations such as, 'Keep a careful eye on your finances and the rewards will be unexpected', would be seized on and held up as 'proof' if a statement of interest earned on a savings account should arrive in the post that week. "There you are! I'm telling you he's brilliant, this astrologer. Everything he writes is always so accurate!" she would exclaim.

The progression to recommended clairvoyants was a more recent development, surprising given the huge loss she carried with her. There was never any message from her mother, and I don't know if she expected one, though she recounted that her first encounter with the spirit world brought forth her father, asking for her forgiveness. From another, what turned out to be a wholly accurate description of a gifted grandson, yet to be born. I received a similar account of the boy I would give birth to from a different clairvoyant several years before his actual flesh and blood arrival. All the subsequent communications I've had from 'the other side', without exception, mention my younger son by name.

Mum and I shared a belief in the afterlife that we didn't need to explain. My future mother-in law died following a brain haemorrhage on our wedding day. Every anniversary is a reminder that our marriage, like my mother's birth, started with a bewildering and shocking loss for two families.

It didn't stop us making light of the afterlife on occasion, though. "I'll come back and haunt you if you fall out with your brother," she used to say. Underneath the throwaway comment was an agreement that she'd give me a sign from the other side.

That was our deal. Sealed in jest but no longer funny. Be there for me. Please.

The door opened and a middle-aged woman with shoulder length, unnaturally black hair invited me in. Piercing green eyes locked onto mine. A silky patterned scarf, in mystic mauve was coiled around her neck, the two ends tied together over a plain black sweater. A ginger cat yawned, meowed and stretched itself between us. But for the colour of the cat and possibly the woman's blue jeans, the first impression was verging on witchy cliché. I tried to put that thought from my mind and followed her to a living room, taking a seat as indicated, at a wooden table. The cat followed us in and promptly sat on my feet. The room was large but sparsely furnished with a nondescript sofa and black rug.

"I'm going to put the cat in the kitchen. She'll only be a distraction when she starts talking. She's a talkative type, aren't you?"

Right on cue the cat demonstrated her conversational abilities and was shushed back through the open door. Good. I was anxious to get on with it.

The woman, her name was Lorraine, asked me to place both hands on the table, palms facing down. With her hands on mine she spent some time, on what she called, 'checking in'. "You have a powerful receptivity to the spirit world yourself," she told me.

"You should allow your psychic ability to guide you, more than you do."

I should. I can see into people's hearts and my instincts are invariably correct. The unreliable, duplicitous, envious or plain evil appear in dayglow colour to me, when they are invisible to others. Sooner or later they reveal their true selves and then my friends or family members will remember that I'd voiced doubts, or even had a bad feeling about so and so from the start.

I was careful not to give prompts to my history or circumstances and Lorraine reminded me not to help her in any way. She told me I was living through a challenging transition, disruptive, but temporary and that this would resolve itself by 2018. A project I'd started, would take up more and more of my time. I had already started writing this book. The countryside would be significant in the next two years and she could see me in a garden. This environment, she kept insisting will do me a lot of good. At this point I knew the next nine months would be spent in Dubai, but where we would live after that was unknown. Finding a permanent home back in the UK when we returned was never far from my thoughts, but the countryside? I had no interest in rural life or gardening. We both liked towns and cities. She mentioned a young person, male, a close, living relative, a significant time of year and the letter J. Yes, that'll be, my younger son.

Lorraine closed her eyes and after a minute or so she spoke again but this time with more clarity. The spirits she described sounded familiar, or rather their behaviour reminded me of people I once knew. I held my breath. "I'm finding this quite hard to interpret but I have a man and woman here," she said. "They're both talking to me at once and I really wish they wouldn't. Let me see if I can just tune into one at a time. There was a pause. "That's better. The man has stopped and he's stepped back to give the woman her own space."

I already knew what Lorraine was about to say. Her green eyes were open and met mine.

"I need to tell you about this woman. She's very glamorous and takes great care with her appearance. I'm getting the impression that she's your mother. But you aren't her only child.

"There's a much younger woman standing next to your mother now. I'm not sure who she is but there is a strong emotional bond between you." Lorraine closed her eyes and there was a few moments of silence.

"When the spirit world shows me flowers I usually tell people to buy the flower I see and think of the person that has passed," she said at last.

My mind was already drifting towards a purchase. There was a place near the station.

"I can see a flower but I believe I am being shown a person's name," she said. "The young woman with your mother is called Rose."

All the air seemed to have been sucked from my lungs. Lorraine was saying something else, but my brain was struggling to keep up.

"Your mother wants me to tell you something important."

Something for me and me alone. I closed my eyes and felt the warmth from Lorraine's hands on mine.

"She says she knows she didn't do everything right."

******

In September 2017 we returned to the UK for good and, for a few months, lived in Limehouse, East London while we searched for a permanent home. We looked in several different areas of the UK and at many houses before we found the right one. We chose a house but sometimes I think it chose us. The location is quite unlike any other place we have lived in, as many of our friends remark when they come to visit. It's rural. Peaceful. There is a beautiful garden.

7

East London, 2017

We left Dubai in 2017 to return to the UK permanently. Through a series of co-incidences, fate, divine intervention, or sheer fluke, for a brief period we lived just a five-minute walk away from the very streets my direct ancestors inhabited in their lifetime and a mere bus ride away from their graves.

The neighbourhood around the cemetery was unfamiliar to me and the bus driver was new to the job. It was left to the jolly Asian mum at my elbow to point me in the right direction. "Yeah, this bus, takes you down there," she said, bouncing an unsmiling toddler on her hip. Given the time of day she assumed I must be going to the school, but when I said no, the cemetery, her chubby face broke into a broad smile, as if I'd cracked a joke.

Once off the bus, my mobile phone was my guide. The smell of raw spices from the Bengali shop on the corner accompanied me down a residential one-way street of Victorian terraced houses in various states of restoration and neglect. At the far end, a modest entrance belied the solemnity and size of the burial ground. The rear upstairs windows of dozens of nearby homes overlooked a gothic landscape of Hebrew memorials and tributes covering some twenty-five acres.

At ground level, in the older sections of the cemetery, the painted numbers on the ground at the end of each row, that once provided helpful guidance, had all but faded away. In my haste to find my way I lost count so retraced my steps and started again. I thought I was alone but a murmur, just audible, made me wonder if I was being followed. I kept looking over my shoulder, but no one else was in sight. Then the penny dropped. The unnerving sound was a recording, triggered by my movement along the path. A ghostly voice, whispering the number in the absence of signage, was designed to assist, rather than frighten the visitor. Paying more attention to my benign guide, I took a left turn off the path.

Many of the graves bore visible signs of their great age through decades of abandonment. Weather damage had taken its toll, causing some of the headstones to lean over at odd angles. The ground was uneven, the way ahead, narrow. I slowed down, scanning each memorial for names, twisting and turning to avoid the slabs keeling towards me at waist height, like drunks. I straightened up, looked to my right and stopped, my involuntary gasp breaking the silence. The name leapt out at me. Rose. This was the grave I'd come for.

The sheer number of people named on this headstone was shocking, each one cut to the core with sorrow and shock at the premature death of one of their own. The lengthy inscription, testament to the grief of the people that had to carry on without her, and a poignant reminder of a time when complications arising from pregnancy and childbirth ended at the cemetery.

Two stones placed at the edge of the memorial suggested someone had been here before me. Mum told me she only found the strength to visit this grave once, leaning on David for support.

Those stones, left in keeping with Jewish custom, was the evidence.

I crouched down to photograph the fading words and something else came into view. The photo momentarily forgotten I read the inscription on a small marble pot, now black with age. Made on a child's behalf, all those years ago, it said, *'A loving token to my dear Mother from Sylvia'*.

A few rows away, I found Hetty's grave. Rose and Hetty were close in death as in life. Weakened from the shock of losing her precious sister, Hetty contracted TB two years later. She left a widower and their two children, Leslie and Harold, both under five years of age. Jane and Hyman, Rose and Hetty's heartbroken parents outlived both their daughters by almost twenty years.

The information left on the gravestones of a few more players in this story speaks their truth. Boy's mother, Miriam lived to eighty-three but her first-born son was missing from the final roll call of mourning children on her elaborate memorial. History sadly repeated itself as Boy's gravestone revealed he was father to only two daughters, not three. His beloved grandmother, Elizabeth, died in her sixties in 1932. Two-year-old Sylvia Rose is named on her gravestone as both a grandchild and great-grandchild, which, though unusual, was indeed the case.

On the bus back to Stepney Green, I thought about the changes to the infrastructure that have taken place there since the end of the Second World War. Despite this, and even with the latest Crossrail development, so many historic buildings and landmarks either remain, or bear evidence of what they once were. The historical diversity of this area is celebrated, well documented, archived and tangible. The old Jewish past is embedded in the stones beneath my feet, in the wind blowing through the trees in the municipal gardens and in the memories of those whose families moved out to the suburbs or decided to remain.

Demolition and the subsequent rebuilding programmes resulted in the reconfiguration of some streets and much was swept away, but the stuff of past lives lived is still evident. If I stop to look at notable decorative features, old brickwork, and original lettering, what I see, they also saw.

Mum often mentioned the clock tower at Stepney Green as a landmark she remembered from childhood and it is there still. Perhaps she even came as a tot, hand in hand with Becky and Jack to watch the spectacle when it arrived by steam wagon to be installed.

At dusk, one breezy autumn day I passed once more along Hayfield Passage, the dreamy cobbled lane leading to Mile End Road. The blue-tinted cobbles were disappearing under a covering of falling leaves from the overhanging trees. Every so often the wind held them in its grasp, only to let them go again, leaving golden piles for walkers to crunch through. The whispering souls of the long departed were surely here, in the flying leaves, not in the stillness and isolation of the graveyard. Echoes of children's tiny voices, just audible through the years, floated back to me above the railings of what was once Stepney Green Jewish School. A shadow flickered over the cobbles and for a moment I fancied I saw the spirit of a broken-hearted young man, carrying his baby daughter in his arms.

As I lingered there, lost in the past, two women in headscarves, pushing buggies, made their way along the lane to the main road,

266

the hems of their long coverings, caressing the leaves on the ground. I turned and watched the women go, the streetlights illuminating their chattering profiles. This was their place and their history to make now. The wind picked up, carrying small handfuls of leaves up and over the cobbles. As the wind dropped, the leaves fell one by one on the ground behind them, as randomly as life itself.

Postscript

I was not able to establish all the facts concerning Rose's short life and tragic death, but with the help of knowledgeable individuals I have attempted a fictional version of events, given the known historical and cultural background.

Rose became very real to me when I read the details contained in her marriage and death certificates. It transpired that she had not died shortly after giving birth from heart failure, as the vague story handed down to my mother implied. The death certificate states Rose died of post-partum eclampsia, three days after giving birth. Prompted by a dangerously high blood pressure, the condition causes convulsions and damage to vital organs. It's likely that this was the outcome in my grandmother's case. Given the circumstances and the times, my mother's safe entry into the world at home, was miraculous and owes much to the midwife in attendance, and the many like her, providing high quality maternity care across the East End at that time.

The death certificate also shows that Rose died in hospital, indicating that her symptoms were recognised and treated. Unfortunately, the drugs available to prevent convulsions and treat high blood pressure were far less effective in 1930. Post-partum eclampsia can still claim the mother's life today if the symptoms are not treated promptly.

One question remains unanswered. Rose died in St Mary's Hospital, Paddington, far from her home in Stepney Green and the medical facilities on her doorstep. I sought some expert opinions on this anomaly. One suggested that St Mary's would have been considered the best option for treatment in 1930, especially if Rose had been seen by a consultant there at an earlier stage of pregnancy. Another said an emergency case would have been taken by ambulance to the nearest hospital and not across London to another. Even a sedated transfer from East to West London in 1930 would have been considered far too dangerous for a woman in her condition. Patient records might have shed some light on this mystery but none covering this period at St Mary's are still in existence.

Post-partum eclampsia and the same tragic outcome featured in an episode of the television series Downton Abbey. Ironically, my mother was an avid fan of this series but was probably unaware that apart from the obvious differences in social class, Lady Sybil Crawley's death following childbirth, mirrored her own family tragedy.

The significance of such a fundamental loss on my mother, and therefore myself cannot be denied, but it was never examined in my mother's lifetime. When I stood alone at Rose's graveside, in a vast cemetery in East London, one miserable November day, the gap in both our lives was laid bare. Circumstances and human frailty cheated us both, of the mother and grandmother that could have bound us together. Rose's death at the age of just twenty-five, and the events that followed, rippled down the years, muddling, muddying and stunting our relationship. We loved each other deeply but we didn't know how to show it. I always felt my mother needed mothering, but I wasn't the one to do it. I was still an insecure child, desperate for my mother's approval, in my forties. In some ways I'm still seeking it. It was only after she'd died that I learned from others how proud of me she really was. Within these pages I tried to make sense of it all and give Rose a longer life than she had, keeping faith with the sentiment still visible on her headstone.

'You are not forgotten Rose dear,
Nor shall you ever be,
As long and life and memory last,
We will remember thee'.

Acknowledgements

Sylvia Freedman, my late mother, who wrote down some of the details of her childhood and growing up, 'for her children and grandchildren'. Her document titled, *Just for the Record*, is the touchstone for this book.

Sheila Barton, for investigating my family tree. You lit the spark that made me want to tell this story.

Debra Paul-Burgess, Sandra Carden, Kirsten Decker, Susan Dibden, H K Frost, Linda MacConnell, Amanda Olsen, Dhooleka Raj, and the late Holly Warah of Dubai Writers Group for your inspiration and helpful feedback on early drafts.

Rachel Kolsky, for showing me the areas of the East End associated with my family. I cherish those places now. Thank you for sharing your passion for history and cake with me.

For answering my questions and pointing me to more useful information, much thanks, Dr Lara Marks, Dr Nick Beech, Jacki Antonovich, Sandra Dawson, Andrew Tomkins, Kevin Brown, Steve Morris, Ronnie Fraser, Mark J Nagle, Elizabeth Granger, Shani Doffman and Graham Barker. Staff at Tower Hamlets Local History and Archive and Richard Meunier and Daniel Heather at Barts Health NHS Trust Archives.

David Taylor @ThEditors, Inglebooks and IC Design for their expertise and guidance.

271

To my brother, Simon Miller for his support and to Tim, Tom and Jack, the three most important grown-ups in my life. You remain behind the scenes in much of this story, but I want you to know that I couldn't have written any of it without your support, advice, patience, encouragement and love.

About the Author

Ruth Badley graduated from the Central School of Speech and Drama in 1978 and taught in secondary schools in London before moving to South Australia, where she worked in adult migrant education, specifically with Vietnamese and Cambodian refugees.

Later she pursued a successful second career as a journalist and was the arts and food writer for Ackrill Newspapers in North Yorkshire for many years. She currently runs her own public relations and freelance writing consultancy for clients in the geospatial industry.

Ruth wrote and directed *Just Playing* for Dubai's Short and Sweet Theatre Festival in 2016. *Where Are The Grown-Ups?* is her first full length work.

She has two adult sons and lives in rural Essex with her husband, Tim.

Website: www.ruthbadley.com
Twitter: @RuthBadleyPR

Printed in Great Britain
by Amazon